Aviation Maintenan

Certification Series

NO COST REVISION/UPDATE SUBSCRIPTION PROGRAM

Complete EASA Part-66 Aviation Maintenance Technician Certification Series

NO COST REVISION/UPDATE PROGRAM

Aircraft Technical Book Company is offering a revision/update program to our customers who purchase an EASA Module from the EASA Aviation Maintenance Technician Certification Series. The update is good for two (2) years from time of registration of any EASA Module or EASA bundled kits. If a revision occurs within two (2) years from date of registration, we will send you the revised pages FREE of cost to the registered email. Go to the link provided at the bottom of this page and fill out the form to be included in the EASA Revision/Update Subscription Program. In an effort to provide quality customer service please let us know if your email you register with changes so we can update our records.

If you have any questions about this process please send an email to: *techsupport@actechbooks.com*

HERE'S HOW IT WORKS

1. All EASA Module Series textbooks contain an EASA subscription page explaining the subscription update process and provide a web site link to register for the EASA Revision/Update Subscription Program.
2. Go to the link provided below and fill out the web based form with your *first and last name, current email address, and school* if applicable.
3. From the time of purchase, if a revision occurs to the Module you have registered for, a revised PDF file containing the pages with edits will be sent to the registered email provided.
4. Please note that we try to keep our records as current as possible. If your email address provided at time of registration changes please let us know as soon as possible so we can update your account.
5. This service is FREE of charge for two (2) years from date of registration.

LINK TO REGISTER FOR REVISION/UPDATE PROGRAM
http://www.actechbooks.com/easasub/m09

MODULE 09A

FOR B1 & B2 CERTIFICATION

HUMAN FACTORS

Aviation Maintenance Technician Certification Series

COMPLIANT WITH

EASA
European Aviation Safety Agency

EASA PART 66/147

AIRCRAFT
TECHNICAL
BOOK COMPANY

72413 U.S. Hwy 40
Tabernash, CO 80478-0270 USA

www.actechbooks.com

+1 970 726-5111

AVIATION MAINTENANCE TECHNICIAN CERTIFICATION SERIES

Author   Nancy Gold

Contributor   James W. Allen, MF, MPH - Working Healthy - Always

Layout/Design   Michael Amrine

Government Resources:

Australian Government, Civil Aviation Safety Authority, Safety Behaviors, Human Factors, Resource Guide for Engineers

Federal Aviation Administration - Dr. William B. Johnson (FAA)

Occupational Safety and Health Administration (OSHA) - *https://www.osha.gov*

Other Resources:

Learning from Experience #2 - *chirp-mems.co-uk*

Version # - Effective Date 11.01.2018

To order books or for Customer Service, please call +1 970 726-5111.

www.actechbooks.com

Printed in the United States of America

ISBN 978-1941144824

For comments or suggestions about this book, please call or write to:
1.970.726.5111 | comments@actechbooks.com

WELCOME

The publishers of this Aviation Maintenance Technician Certification Series welcome you to the world of aviation maintenance. As you move towards EASA certification, you are required to gain suitable knowledge and experience in your chosen area. Qualification on basic subjects for each aircraft maintenance license category or subcategory is accomplished in accordance with the following matrix. Where applicable, subjects are indicated by an "X" in the column below the license heading.

For other educational tools created to prepare candidates for licensure, contact Aircraft Technical Book Company.

We wish you good luck and success in your studies and in your aviation career!

REVISION LOG

VERSION	EFFECTIVE DATE	DESCRIPTION OF CHANGE
001	2015 01	Module Creation and Release
002	2018 10	Typographic and Layout Updates – No Content Change

FORWARD

PART-66 and the Acceptable Means of Compliance (AMC) and Guidance Material (GM) of the European Aviation Safety Agency (EASA), Appendix 1 establishes the Basic Knowledge Requirements for those seeking an aircraft maintenance license. The information in this Module of the Aviation Maintenance Technical Certification Series published by Aircraft Technical Book Company meets or exceeds the breadth and depth of knowledge subject matter referenced in Appendix 1 of the Implementing Rules. However, the order of the material presented is at the discretion of the editor in an effort to convey the required knowledge in the most sequential and comprehensible manner. Knowledge levels required for Category A1, B1, B2, and B3 aircraft maintenance licenses remain unchanged from those listed in Appendix 1 Basic Knowledge Requirements. Tables from Appendix 1 Basic Knowledge Requirements are reproduced at the beginning of each module in the series and again at the beginning of each Sub-Module.

How numbers are written in this book:
This book uses the International Civil Aviation Organization (ICAO) standard of writing numbers. This method displays large numbers by adding a space between each group of 3 digits. This is opposed to the American method which uses commas and the European method which uses periods. For example, the number one million is expressed as so:

ICAO Standard	1 000 000
European Standard	1.000.000
American Standard	1,000,000

SI Units:
The International System of Units (SI) developed and maintained by the General Conference of Weights and Measures (CGPM) shall be used as the standard system of units of measurement for all aspects of international civil aviation air and ground operations.

Prefixes:
The prefixes and symbols listed in the table below shall be used to form names and symbols of the decimal multiples and submultiples of International System of Units (SI) units.

MULTIPLICATION FACTOR		PREFIX	SYMBOL
1 000 000 000 000 000 000	$= 10^{18}$	exa	E
1 000 000 000 000 000	$= 10^{15}$	peta	P
1 000 000 000 000	$= 10^{12}$	tera	T
1 000 000 000	$= 10^{9}$	giga	G
1 000 000	$= 10^{6}$	mega	M
1 000	$= 10^{3}$	kilo	k
100	$= 10^{2}$	hecto	h
10	$= 10^{1}$	deca	da
0.1	$= 10^{-1}$	deci	d
0.01	$= 10^{-2}$	centi	c
0.001	$= 10^{-3}$	milli	m
0.000 001	$= 10^{-6}$	micro	μ
0.000 000 001	$= 10^{-9}$	nano	n
0.000 000 000 001	$= 10^{-12}$	pico	p
0.000 000 000 000 001	$= 10^{-15}$	femto	f
0.000 000 000 000 000 001	$= 10^{-18}$	atto	a

International System of Units (SI) Prefixes

EASA LICENSE CATEGORY CHART

Module Number and Title		A1 Airplane Turbine	B1.1 Airplane Turbine	B1.2 Airplane Piston	B1.3 Helicopter Turbine	B2 Avionics
1	Mathematics	X	X	X	X	X
2	Physics	X	X	X	X	X
3	Electrical Fundamentals	X	X	X	X	X
4	Electronic Fundamentals		X	X	X	X
5	Digital Techniques / Electronic Instrument Systems	X	X	X	X	X
6	Materials and Hardware	X	X	X	X	X
7A	Maintenance Practices	X	X	X	X	X
8	Basic Aerodynamics	X	X	X	X	X
9A	Human Factors	X	X	X	X	X
10	Aviation Legislation	X	X	X	X	X
11A	Turbine Aeroplane Aerodynamics, Structures and Systems	X	X			
11B	Piston Aeroplane Aerodynamics, Structures and Systems			X		
12	Helicopter Aerodynamics, Structures and Systems				X	
13	Aircraft Aerodynamics, Structures and Systems					X
14	Propulsion					X
15	Gas Turbine Engine	X	X		X	
16	Piston Engine			X		
17A	Propeller	X	X	X		

GENERAL KNOWLEDGE REQUIREMENTS
MODULE 09A SYLLABUS AS OUTLINED IN PART-66, APPENDIX 1

Level 1

A familiarization with the principal elements of the subject.

Objectives:
  a. The applicant should be familiar with the basic elements of the subject.
  b. The applicant should be able to give a simple description of the whole subject, using common words and examples.
  c. The applicant should be able to use typical terms.

Level 2

A general knowledge of the theoretical and practical aspects of the subject and an ability to apply that knowledge.

Objectives:
  a. The applicant should be able to understand the theoretical fundamentals of the subject.
  b. The applicant should be able to give a general description of the subject using, as appropriate, typical examples.
  c. The applicant should be able to use mathematical formula in conjunction with physical laws describing the subject.
  d. The applicant should be able to read and understand sketches, drawings and schematics describing the subject.
  e. The applicant should be able to apply his knowledge in a practical manner using detailed procedures.

Level 3

A detailed knowledge of the theoretical and practical aspects of the subject and a capacity to combine and apply the separate elements of knowledge in a logical and comprehensive manner.

Objectives:
  a. The applicant should know the theory of the subject and interrelationships with other subjects.
  b. The applicant should be able to give a detailed description of the subject using theoretical fundamentals and specific examples.
  c. The applicant should understand and be able to use mathematical formula related to the subject.
  d. The applicant should be able to read, understand and prepare sketches, simple drawings and schematics describing the subject.
  e. The applicant should be able to apply his knowledge in a practical manner using manufacturer's instructions.
  f. The applicant should be able to interpret results from various sources and measurements and apply corrective action where appropriate.

9.1 - General
The need to take human factors into account;
Incidents attributable to human factors/human error;
"Murphy's" law.

B1: 2 · B2: 2

9.2 - Human Performance and Limitations
Vision;
Hearing;
Information processing;
Attention and perception;
Memory;
Claustrophobia and physical access.

B1: 2 · B2: 2

9.3 - Social Psychology
Responsibility: individual and group;
Motivation and demotivation;
Peer pressure;
"Culture" issues;
Team working;
Management, supervision and leadership.

B1: 1 · B2: 1

9.4 - Factors Affecting Performance
Fitness/health;
Stress: domestic and work related;
Time pressure and deadlines;
Workload: overload and underload;
Sleep and fatigue, shiftwork;
Alcohol, medication, drug abuse.

B1: 2 · B2: 2

9.5 - Physical Environment
Noise and fumes;
Illumination;
Climate and temperature;
Motion and vibration;
Working environment.

B1: 1 · B2: 1

9.6 - Tasks
Physical work;
Repetitive tasks;
Visual inspection;
Complex systems.

B1: 1 · B2: 1

9.7 - *Communication*
Within and between teams;
Work logging and recording;
Keeping up to date, currency;
Dissemination of information.

	B1	B2
9.7	2	2

9.8 - *Human Error*
Error models and theories;
Types of error in maintenance tasks;
Implications of errors (i.e. accidents);
Avoiding and managing errors.

	B1	B2
9.8	2	2

9.9 - *Hazards in the Workplace*
Recognizing and avoiding hazards;
Dealing with emergencies.

	B1	B2
9.9	2	2

HUMAN FACTORS

SUB-MODULE 01
GENERAL

SUB-MODULE 02
HUMAN PERFORMANCE AND LIMITATIONS

CONTENTS

SUB-MODULE 03
SOCIAL PSYCHOLOGY

SUB-MODULE 04
FACTORS AFFECTING PERFORMANCE

CONTENTS

CONTENTS

HUMAN FACTORS

GENERAL

SUB-MODULE 01

PART-66 SYLLABUS LEVELS

	CERTIFICATION CATEGORY →	B1	B2

Sub-Module 01

GENERAL

Knowledge Requirements

9.1 - General

	B1	B2
The need to take human factors into account;	2	2
Incidents attributable to human factors/human error;		
"Murphy's" law.		

9.1 - GENERAL

INTRODUCTION

Why are human conditions such as fatigue, complacency, and stress, so important in aviation maintenance? These conditions, along with many others, are called human factors. Human factors directly cause or contribute to many aviation accidents. It is universally agreed that at least 80 percent of maintenance related incidents involve human factors. If they are not prevented, and their causes detected, they can cause injuries, wasted time, and even accidents. (*Figure 1-1*)

THE NEED TO TAKE HUMAN FACTORS INTO ACCOUNT

Aviation safety relies heavily on maintenance. When it is not done correctly, it contributes to a significant proportion of accidents and incidents. Some examples of maintenance errors may include; parts installed incorrectly, missing parts, or necessary checks not being performed. In comparison to many other threats to aviation safety, the mistakes of an Aviation Maintenance Technician (AMT) can be more difficult to detect.

Often times, these mistakes are present but not visible and have the potential to remain latent, affecting the safe operation of aircraft for long periods of time. AMTs are confronted with a set of human factors unique within aviation. Often times, AMTs are working in the evening or early morning hours, in confined spaces, on platforms that are up high, or in a variety of adverse temperature/humidity conditions. The work can be physically strenuous, yet also requiring a high degree of attention to detail. (*Figure 1-2*)

Because of the nature of maintenance tasks, AMTs commonly spend more time preparing for a task than actually carrying it out. Proper documentation of all maintenance work is a key element, and AMTs also typically spend as much time updating maintenance logs as they do performing the work.

Human factors and how they affect people are very important to aviation maintenance. Such awareness can lead to improved quality, an environment that ensures continuing worker and aircraft safety, and a more involved and responsible work force. More specifically, the reduction of even minor errors can provide measurable benefits including cost reductions, fewer missed deadlines, reduction in work related injuries, reduction of warranty claims, and reduction in more significant events that can be traced back to maintenance error.

It is apparent that anticipated or abnormal medical conditions influence the AMTs work. Reduction in vision is a signpost of aging that is anticipated in all AMTs over the age of 50 years. It compromises the visual

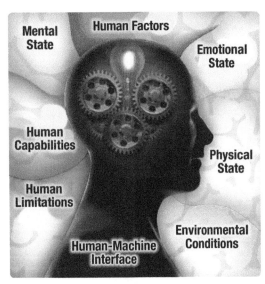

Figure 1-1. The above human factors and how they affect people are very important. Awareness of their influence can help control possible accidents

Figure 1-2. Aviation maintenance technicians have many distractions and must focus on detail.

inspection of aircraft. Obesity is an abnormal medical condition that leads to multiple metabolic changes. It produces behaviors described by The Dirty Dozen of human factors. These consequences from normal aging or abnormal medical conditions are classified as Latent Medical or Environmental Conditions (LMEC).

THE ORGANIZATIONAL ENVIRONMENT

HOW DOES YOUR ORGANIZATION STACK UP?		
POSITIVE ORGANIZATIONAL CHARACTERISTICS		
There are sufficient staff appropriately licensed to cover the workload.	Yes	No
The organization never encourages shortcuts or procedure violations.	Yes	No
Management acts quickly to fix unsafe situations.	Yes	No
Staff are encouraged to report errors and unsafe situations.	Yes	No
The company has a 'just culture' policy. Incidents are investigated to identify why they occurred, not whom to blame.	Yes	No
Staff receive human factors training.	Yes	No
NEGATIVE ORGANIZATIONAL CHARACTERISTICS		
There is an extreme 'can-do' culture. Staff do whatever it takes to get a job done on time.	Yes	No
Tasks are routinely performed according to 'norms' (informal work practices), rather than documented procedures.	Yes	No
Staff are often required to work excessive hours.	Yes	No
Work is done differently when there is time pressure.	Yes	No
Shortages of spares or equipment often lead to workarounds.	Yes	No
There is rapid staff turnover, or many inexperienced personnel.	Yes	No

INCIDENTS RELATED TO HUMAN FACTORS

The following are major incidents that have been directly attributed to human factors.

CASE STUDY: ALOHA AIRLINES FLIGHT 243
Complacency is identified as one of "The Dirty Dozen" of aircraft maintenance human factors. (Discussed in full detail in Sub-Module 09, along with other error models). The Dirty Dozen are 12 identified human factors that lead to maintenance errors. Complacency is at the top of this list and is the deadliest of the 12 factors. This is demonstrated by the tragic Aloha Flight 243, which took place on April 28, 1988. Complacency with the state of aging aircraft was exposed as the cause of the accident and this event became the watershed accident that would bring much needed change.

Aloha Airlines Flight 243 (AQ 243, AAH 243) was a scheduled Aloha Airlines flight between Hilo and Honolulu in Hawaii. On April 28, 1988, a Boeing 737-297 serving the flight suffered extensive damage after an explosive decompression in flight, but was able to land safely at Kahului Airport on Maui. There was one fatality, a member of the flight crew who was swept overboard from the airplane. Another 65 passengers and crew were injured. The safe landing of the aircraft despite the substantial damage inflicted by the decompression established Aloha Airlines Flight 243 as a significant event in the history of aviation, with far reaching effects on aviation safety policies and procedures. (*Figure 1-3*)

The flight departed Hilo at 13:25 HST on April 28, 1988 with six crew members and 89 passengers, bound for Honolulu. No unusual occurrences were noticed during the predeparture inspection of the aircraft. The aircraft had previously completed three round trip flights from Honolulu to Hilo, Maui, and Kauai that day, all which were uneventful. Meteorological conditions were checked but no advisories for weather phenomenon occurred along the air route, per Airman's meteorological information or significant meteorological information. The captain was an experienced pilot with 8 500 flight hours; 6 700 of those were in Boeing 737s. The first officer had significant experience flying 737s, having logged 3 500 of her total 8 000 flight hours in them

No unusual occurrences were reported during the takeoff and ascent. Around 13:48, as the aircraft reached its normal flight altitude of 24 000 feet (7 300 m) about 23 nautical miles (43 km) south southeast of Kahului, Maui, a small section on the left side of the roof ruptured with a "whooshing" sound. The captain felt the aircraft roll left and right, and the controls went

Figure 1-3. Aloha Airlines Flight 243; A watershed moment in aviation maintenance history that brought about much needed change in aviation maintenance. It was recognized that complacency in the state of aging aircraft was the main contributing factor to this accident.

loose. The first officer noticed pieces of gray insulation floating over the cabin. The door to the cockpit was gone so the captain could look behind him and see blue sky. The resulting explosive decompression tore off a large section of the roof, consisting of the entire top half of the aircraft skin extending from just behind the cockpit to the forewing area.

The first officer was flying the plane at the time of the incident. After discovering the damage, the captain took over and steered the plane to the closest airport, on Maui Island. Thirteen minutes later, the crew performed an emergency landing on Kahului Airport's Runway 02. Upon landing, the crew deployed the aircraft's emergency evacuation slides and evacuated passengers from the aircraft quickly. In all, 65 people were reported injured, eight seriously.

Investigation

The main factor was the failure of the Aloha Airlines maintenance program to detect the presence of significant disbonding and fatigue damage.

Contributing causes were the failure of Aloha Airlines management to supervise properly its maintenance forces. The failure of the Federal Aviation Administration (FAA) to properly evaluate the Aloha Airlines maintenance program, and to assess the airlines inspection and quality control deficiencies. The failure of the FAA to require Airworthiness Directive AD 87.21-08 inspection of all

the lap joints proposed by Boeing Alert Service Bulletin SB 737.53A1039; and the lack of a complete terminating action (neither generated by Boeing nor required by the FAA) after the discovery of early production difficulties in the Boeing 737 cold bond lap joint which resulted in low bond durability, corrosion, and premature fatigue cracking.

Safety Recommendations

Investigator's made eighteen *Safety Recommendations*.

FAA Recommendations

- Provide specific guidance and proper engineering support to principal maintenance inspectors to evaluate modifications of airline maintenance programs and operations specifications, which propose segmenting major maintenance inspections.
- Revise the regulation governing the certification of aviation maintenance technical schools and licensing of airframe and power plant mechanics to require that curriculum and testing requirements include modern aviation industry technology.
- Require formal certification and recurrent training of aviation maintenance inspectors performing nondestructive inspection functions. Formal training should include apprenticeship and periodic skill demonstration.

AIRCRAFT
TECHNICAL
BOOK COMPANY

- Develop a continuing inspection program for those Boeing 737 airplanes that have incorporated lap joint termination action (protruding head solid fasteners installed in the upper row of all lap splices) to detect any fatigue cracking that my develop in the middle or lower rows of fuselage lap joint fasteners holes (for both the inner and outer skin panels) or the adjacent tear strap fastener holes. Additionally, to define the types of inspections, inspection intervals, and corrective actions needed for continuing airworthiness.
- Develop a model program for a comprehensive corrosion control program to be included in each operator's approved maintenance program.
- Issue an airworthiness directive for Boeing 737 airplanes equipped with carbon steel control cables to inspect the cables for evidence of corrosion and if there is evidence, to accomplish the actions set forth in Boeing Service letter 737-SL-76.2-A.
- Enhance stature and performance of the principal inspectors through; (1) formal management training and guidance, (2) Greater encouragement and backing by headquarters of efforts by principal inspectors to secure the implementation by carriers of levels of safety above the regulatory minimums, (3) Improve accountability for quality of the surveillance; (4) Additional headquarters assistance in standardizing surveillance activities.
- Discontinue classification of fuselage skin as "malfunction evident" or "damage obvious" on supplemental structurally significant items in the damage obvious category for possible inclusion in the supplementary inspection program.
- Issue an air carrier operations bulletin for all air carrier flight training departments to review the accident scenario and reiterate the need to assess airplane airworthiness as stated in the operators manual before taking action that my cause further damage or breakup of a damaged airframe.

Aloha Airlines Recommendations
- Revise the maintenance program to recognize the high time high cycles nature of the fleet operations and initiate maintenance inspection and overhaul concepts based on realistic and acceptable calendar and flight cycle intervals.
- Initiate a corrosion prevention and control program designed to afford maximum protection from the effects of harsh operating environments.

- Revise and upgrade the technical division manpower and organization to provide the necessary management, quality assurance, engineering, technical training and production personnel to maintain high level of airworthiness of the fleet.
- Assist member air carriers to establish maintenance department engineering services to evaluate maintenance practices including structural repair, compliance with airworthiness directives and service bulletins, performance of inspection and quality assurance sections, and overall effectiveness of continuing airworthiness programs.

Related to "The Dirty Dozen"
- Complacency with the state of aging aircraft – **Complacency**
- Working under pressure – **Pressure**
- Inspections done at night; circadian rhythm upset –**Fatigue**
- Inspectors suspended by safety harnesses – **Lack of Resource**s
- Required to inspect 1 300 rivets – **Pressure**
- Documentation is complicated and subject to interpretation – **Lack of Knowledge**
- Engineering Dept was outsourced – **Lack of Communication, Lack of Teamwork**
- Hangar lighting designed for DC-3's – **Lack of Resources**
- Lack of adequate manpower – **Fatigue**
- Lack of knowledge - just two hours of NDT training – **Lack of Knowledge**

CASE STUDY: BRITISH AIRWAYS BAC-111; WINDSCREEN BLOWOUT

The aircraft, captained by 42 year old, who had logged 11 050 flight hours, and copiloted by 39 year old, who had logged 7 500 flight hours, was a BAC One Eleven Series. The aircraft took off at 7:20am local time, with 81 passengers, four cabin crew and two flight crew. Copilot handled a routine takeoff, and relinquished control as the plane established itself in its climb. Both pilots subsequently released their shoulder harnesses, while the pilot loosened his lap belt as well.

The plane had climbed to 17 300 feet (5 270 m) over Didcot, Oxfordshire. Suddenly, there was a loud bang, and the fuselage quickly filled with condensation. The left windscreen, on the captain's side of the cockpit, had separated from the forward fuselage. The Captain

AIRCRAFT TECHNICAL BOOK COMPANY

was jerked out of his seat by the rushing air and forced head first out of the cockpit, his knees snagging onto the flight controls.

The door to the flight deck was blown out onto the radio and navigation console, blocking the throttle control which caused the plane to continue gaining speed as they descended, while papers and other debris in the passenger cabin began blowing towards the cockpit. On the flight deck, the flight attendant quickly latched his hands onto the captain's belt; another flight attendant began to reassure passengers, secure loose objects, and take up emergency positions.

The copilot eventually received clearance from air traffic control to land at Southampton. The aircraft had landed safely on Runway 02, where the passengers immediately disembarked from the front and rear stairs, and emergency crews retrieved the captain.

Investigation

Accident investigators found that a replacement windscreen had been installed 27 hours before the flight, and that the procedure had been approved by the shift maintenance manager. However, 84 of the 90 windscreen retention bolts were 0.026 inches (0.66 mm) too small in diameter, while the remaining six were 0.1 inches (2.5 mm) too short. (**Figure 1-4**)

The investigation revealed that the previous windscreen had been fitted with incorrect bolts. Because the plane was due to take off soon and there was a tight schedule, in order to save time, the shift maintenance manager replaced the bolts on a "like for like" basis without referencing the maintenance documentation. The air pressure

difference between the cabin and the outside during the flight proved to be too much, leading to the failure of the windscreen. The incident also brought to attention a design flaw in the aircraft. Securing the windscreen from the outside of the aircraft put a greater pressure on the bolts than if they were secured from the inside.

Investigators found the British Airways Birmingham Airport shift maintenance manager responsible for installing the incorrect bolts during the windscreen replacement, and for failing to follow official British Airways' policies. They also found fault with British Airways' policies, which should have required testing or verification by another individual for this critical task. Finally, investigators found the local Birmingham Airport management responsible for not directly monitoring the shift maintenance manager's working practices.

Safety Recommendations

Investigators made eight safety recommendations in the final accident report.

British Airways Recommendations

- Review their quality assurance system and encourage technicians to provide feedback.
- Review the need to introduce job descriptions and terms of reference for different grades Shift Maintenance Manager and above.
- Review their product sample procedure to achieve independent assessment of standards and to conduct an indepth audit into the work practices at Birmingham Airport.

Civil Aviation Authority Recommendations

- Examine the continued viability of self certification with regards to safety critical tasks on aircraft.
- Review the purpose and scope of the FOI 7 Supervisory Visit.
- Consider the need for the periodic training and testing of technicians.
- Recognize the need for the use of corrective glasses, if prescribed, in association with aircraft engineering tasks.
- Ensure that, prior to the issue of an air traffic control rating, a candidate shall undergo an approved course including training in both the theoretical and practical handling of emergency situations.

Figure 1-4. Incorrect windscreen retention bolts; (too small) led to the windshield blowout.

Related to "The Dirty Dozen"

- There were staff shortages – **Lack of Resources**
- Time pressures existed – **Pressure/Fatigue**
- All the errors occurred at night – **Fatigue**
- Shift or task hand overs were involved
  – **Lack of Communication**
- All involved supervisors doing long hands on tasks
  – **Lack of Teamwork**
- There was an element of a "can do" attitude
  – **Complacency**
- Interruptions occurred – **Distraction**
- There was some failure to use approved data or company procedures
  – **Lack of Knowledge, Lack of Resources**
- Manuals were confusing – **Lack of Resources**
- There was inadequate planning, equipment or spares
  – **Lack of Resources**

CASE STUDY: NOSE WHEEL JAMMED ON DASH-8

While preparing a Dash-8 (DHS-8) aircraft to return to service after major repairs, maintenance technicians noticed that the nose gear was missing a cover plate designed to protect micro switches from dust and stone damage, no spare was available. To help the company meet a deadline, maintenance personnel decided to manufacture a substitute cover plate, without waiting to get engineering approval. The plate was only a protective cover, not a structural component, and this probably led them to believe that manufacturing a similar replacement part would not affect safety.

The original plate was shaped to provide clearance between it and the micro switches and was secured using countersunk screws. Because of the limited manufacturing capability at this maintenance facility, the replacement cover was manufactured from a flat plate and spacers were used to provide similar clearance. The holes in the replacement plate were not drilled to accept countersunk screws and it was secured using washers and hexagonal head bolts. The bolt heads protruded beyond the normal position of the counter sunk screw heads. The difference was sufficient to cause the landing gear to jam in the up position during a test flight following the repairs. (*Figure 1-5*) A retraction test that might have detected the problem was successfully completed before the replacement plate was fitted.

Investigation

Positive gravity maneuvers and a touch and go landing failed to shake the nose gear free. The crew decided to land once all other traffic was clear and emergency

Figure 1-5. A retraction test done after the plate was fitted as opposed to prior, would have prevented damage from this accident.

services were in place. A landing was completed with the aircraft sliding to a stop on its main wheels and nose. The accident investigator noted that a culture of "getting the job done" existed in the company and there was a strong sense of loyalty and motivation among the maintenance staff. The report concluded, "Staff excelled themselves in order to meet deadlines. While this approach is laudable, research and investigation has shown that it can lead to incorrect practices if the appropriate balance is not found".

As described in this example, an awareness of how the physical and organizational environment influences maintenance tasks is an essential part of human factors. If you can identify error producing conditions in your work environment, you will be better prepared to change those things you can change, and deal with those things that are beyond your control.

Related to "The Dirty Dozen"
- Corporate culture – get the job done at all costs – **Pressure**
- Time saving short cuts – **Pressure**
- Lack of spare parts – **Lack of Resource**s
- Retraction test done before replacement part fitted – **Lack of Knowledge, Complacency**

CASE STUDY: FAILURE TO PRESSURIZE AFTER OUTFLOW VALVE LEFT IN OPEN POSITION

Early on the morning of August 14, 2005, a Boeing 737-300 aircraft departed Cyprus for Prague via Athens. About five minutes after takeoff, at an altitude of 12 040 ft. and at a cabin pressure that corresponded to an altitude of 10 000 ft., an aural warning horn sounded. On this type of aircraft, the same aural tone is used to indicate two conditions: Take-off Configuration Warning and Cabin Altitude Warning.

A minute and a half later, with the aircraft still climbing, the captain contacted the company operations center on the company radio frequency and reported that the crew had a takeoff configuration warning. The operations center put a ground technician on the line to communicate with the captain. The technician later reported a confusing conversation in which the captain mentioned a problem with the ventilation cooling fan lights.

Since the message from the captain did not make any sense to the technician, he asked the captain to "confirm that the pressurization panel was selected to AUTO." The captain responded "where are my equipment cooling circuit breakers?" The technician replied "behind the captain's seat".

During the conversation with the company operations center, the passenger oxygen masks deployed as they were designed to do when the cabin altitude exceeded 14 000 ft. The communication between the ground technician and the captain ended as the aircraft climbed through 28 900 ft.

Shortly after, the flight crew is believed to have lost useful consciousness as a result of hypoxia, the aircraft leveled off at 34 000 and continued on its programmed route, eventually entering a programmed holding pattern near Athens. There was no response to radio calls to the aircraft.

F-16 fighters were scrambled to intercept the 737. One of the F-16 pilots observed the aircraft at close range and reported that the captain's seat was vacant, the first officer's seat was occupied by someone who was slumped over the controls, the passenger oxygen masks were dangling, and motionless passengers were seen seated wearing oxygen masks in the cabin. A person who appeared to be a flight attendant was then seen to enter the cockpit and sit in the captain's seat. At around 9:00am, the engines flamed out due to fuel exhaustion and the aircraft crashed into hilly terrain northwest of Athens airport. All the 115 passengers and six crew died.

Investigation
During the previous flight, cabin crew had noticed frozen door seals and noises around the right aft service door, and the flight crew wrote up an entry in the aircraft tech log 'aft service door requires full inspection'.

Between 1:30am and 3:15am, technicians performed a visual inspection of the aft service door and carried out a cabin pressurization leak check. During the leak check, the technician who would later speak with the captain during the flight went to the cockpit to pressurize the aircraft, while another technician stayed in the rear of the aircraft near the R2 door. No defects were found and the log entry was signed off.

The maintenance manual procedure for the cabin pressurization check required the pressurization mode selector in the cockpit to be set to the MAN (Manual) position. The investigation board found that after the pressurization test, the pressurization mode selector was not selected back to AUTO (*Figure 1-6*).

As a result, the aircraft's out flow valve (OFV) remained fixed in the open position, the position it was last left in. The investigation board stated 'Although not a formal omission, it would have been prudent to position the pressurization mode selector back to AUTO'. The board noted that the last action item in the pressurization check procedure stated "Put the airplane back to its initial condition".

Safety Recommendations

The board considered that these instructions were vague because they did not state specifically that the pressurization mode selector must be returned to the AUTO position, although the procedure explicitly required setting that selector to the MAN (manual) position for the test.

During their preflight preparations, the flight crew was required to confirm that all selectors, including the pressurization mode selector, were in their proper positions for flight. The flight crew apparently did not recognize that the pressurization mode selector was set

to MAN instead of AUTO, as required. As a result, the out flow valve (OFV) remained fixed in the open position, and the cabin did not pressurize.

The official accident report provides a much more detailed treatment of the accident and the wider organizational issues that were associated with it, but the vagueness of the maintenance manual instructions was a significant contributing factor.

Related to "The Dirty Dozen"
- Vagueness of manual instructions
  - **Lack of Knowledge, Lack of Resources**

CASE STUDY: MAIN WHEEL INCORRECTLY FITTED

It is all too easy to take for granted the support that exists in a main base environment. The following incident serves as a reminder of the some of the issues experienced at some line stations.

On arrival at main base, the flight crew of a long haul twin engine aircraft reported that one of the main wheel tire pressures was intermittently reading low. On hubcap removal, the wheel nut was seen to be too far down the axle threads, and the locking bolt was barely engaged with the axle nut. The wheel had been changed at the line station prior to the last sector.

The resident line technician discovered a cut in a main wheel tire on his initial walk around and after assessment, felt that the tire was within maintenance manual limits. However, subsequent discussions with customer services and the flight crew led to the decision to change the wheel; nightfall was approaching and the clock was ticking.

The line station in question supported one resident technician with back up from other airlines. The regular back up technician was contacted at home (1.5 hours away from the airport) while the resident technician conscripted a couple of baggage handlers to help with the manual tasks of a wheel change.

Once all the equipment was positioned at the aircraft, the technician started to jack the wheel, at which time the baggage handlers 'disappeared'. The technician then discovered that the jack did not work on air drive and manual jacking was accomplished with support from

Figure 1-6. Pressurization Panel was not reset back to auto.

the refuel technician. By this time the flight crew had arrived and the third flight crew member was assigned to hold a flashlight through all operations, as the ramp lighting was insufficient.

Having sought support from the baggage handlers again, the wheel was removed. After inspecting and regreasing the axle, the new wheel was positioned, minus the spacer, which was still attached to the wheel. The wheel nut was torqued and a spin check carried out. As the cover plate was being fitted, after the tire pressure sensor had been connected, the backup technician arrived to finish the job while the resident technician attended to a further fault on the flight deck.

Investigation
The main contributory factors identified during the investigation were:
- Pressure caused by lone working practices on station.
- Work area inadequately lit.
- Pressure of a delay that could have caused crew to go out of hours.
- No specific cautions or warnings in the maintenance manual to ensure that the spacer was fitted.

Safety Recommendations
With regards to lone working, the line station reviewed its policy and identified that, having one resident technician was sufficient for normal operations as there are plenty of other staff around the aircraft (baggage handlers, refuel technician, etc.) to ensure that safety is maintained. What was lacking was a robust process to ensure that when the resident technician required support, it was readily available. (*Figure 1-7*)

The other lessons recommendation was one of communication. Operational pressure is always going exist but as long as the technician kept everyone abreast of the situation, there should have been no undue pressure to dispatch a less than serviceable aircraft. Commercial pressures must not play a part when it comes to aircraft maintenance practices.

Related to "The Dirty Dozen"
- Pressure caused by lone working practices on station
  – **Lack of Resources, Pressure**
- Work area inadequately lit – **Lack of Resources**
- Pressure of a delay that could have caused crew to go out of hours – **Pressure**
- No specific cautions or warnings in the maintenance manual to ensure that the spacer was fitted
  – **Lack of Knowledge, Lack of Communication**

Figure 1-7. Maintenance requires sufficient personnel.

CASE STUDY: TORCH (FLASHLIGHT) LEFT IN NOSE WHEEL STEERING CABLE RUN

Maintenance errors, as we know, can take various forms from panels being installed incorrectly to inadequate surveillance inspections. This incident relates to the consequences of not accounting for all tooling used after a task has been completed. (*Figure 1-8*)

During taxi out to the runway for a return sector from Europe, the flight crew of a Boeing 737 found the aircraft difficult to control through the rudder pedals. The steering tiller would not return to the neutral (self center) making rudder nose wheel steering "impossible". Inspection of the nose wheel steering mechanism found a torch stuck in the cable run, causing damage to the cable guide wheel bracket and a pulley. Investigation identified that the nose wheel spin brake pads had been replaced the night before but why had the engineers involved failed to remove the torch?

An engineer and two technicians were tasked to work the Boeing 737 but prior to starting their assigned work for the night, they were involved in clearing late evening departure snags. The engineer busied himself with researching a hydraulic leak on an Airbus while the technicians started the spin pad replacement on the aircraft at approximately 3:30am. In addition to the spin pad replacement, the aircraft also had a toilet leak requiring the toilet dump valve to be replaced, so the technicians split the tasks.

The technician arrived at the aircraft, which was parked remotely in the mobile workshop. His original plan was to use separate lighting from the mobile workshop but when he opened the rear doors of the workshop there was a torch lying on the floor. He placed the torch on top of the nose leg and positioned it as best he could to illuminate the task in hand.

During completion of the task involved, the technician inadvertently kicked over a bag of spanners and only after completing the replacement of the spin pads did he pick them up. In doing so, he was momentarily dazzled by the headlamps of the mobile workshop, which was enough to distract from the fact that the torch had not been removed. The technician then assisted his colleague in changing the toilet dump valve as past experience had told him it was a tricky job.

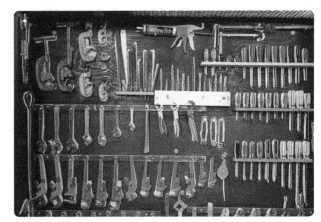

Figure 1-8. All tools need to be accounted for after a task is completed.

After both technicians had completed their work on the Boeing 737, they proceeded to the Airbus and began work on a hydraulic pump change. They did not complete this job in the time available and eventually handed it over to the day shift. The engineer never visited the Boeing 737 as he considered the technicians to be proficient and the assigned tasks relatively straightforward.

Investigation and Recommendations

The main contributory factors identified during the investigation were:

- Time pressure; the technician was aware that work was still outstanding on the Airbus and he needed to give his colleague a hand with changing the toilet dump valve.
- Tool control; there was inadequate control to ensure all tooling was accounted for.
- Inspection; the engineer failed to inspect the replacement of the spin pads prior to signing for the task in the technical log.
- Poorly lit work area: It is worth noting that the 'safety nets' of an engineering preservice check and two flight crew walk around inspections failed to identify the torch, primarily due to the restricted visibility of the nose wheel area, with doors closed, on the Boeing 737.

A fundamentally mundane task could have led to a far more serious incident.

Related to "The Dirty Dozen"

- Time pressure – **Pressure**
- Tool control
  – **Lack of Teamwork, Lack of Awareness**
- Inspection – **Lack of Communication, Pressure, and Lack of Teamwork**

Figure 1-9. Lt. Colonel John Paul Stapp, Gee Whiz Experiment on April 30th, 1947.

- Poorly lit work area – **Lack of Resources**
- Mundane task could have led to a far more serious incident – **Distraction, Complacency**

MURPHY'S LAW

"Whatever Can Go Wrong, Will Go Wrong"

Yes, there really was a Murphy. He was Captain Edward A. Murphy Jr., an Air Force engineer. The saying came from a 1949 experiment at Edwards Air Force Base in California. The experiment was to determine how many G's (force of gravity), a pilot could withstand; the test used a rocket sled nicknamed "Gee Whiz" which simulated the force of an airplane crash. Colonel John Paul Stapp was the volunteer who participated in the rocket sled tests. (***Figure 1-9***)

Captain Murphy attended one of the tests and attached sensors to the colonel. The sensors were capable of measuring the G-force applied when the sled came to a stop, improving the test result data. The first test produced a zero reading; upon examination, it was determined that all four sensors were connected incorrectly. On each of the four sensors, there were two possible ways to connect the wires; and on all four sensors, the wires were hooked up incorrectly!

Murphy was very upset and blamed the technician for the foul up. He supposedly said "If there are two ways to do something, and one will result in disaster, he'll do it that way". *Source: Improbable Research*

Colonel Stapp recognized the importance of Murphy's comments, and when talking to the press, attributed the successes and the sled team's safety record to "Murphy's Law". He explained Murphy's Law as "whatever can go wrong, will go wrong", and if you can anticipate problems, disaster can be averted. (***Figure 1-10***)

Failures in aviation and space exploration can be extremely costly. In one unmanned orbiting vessel, (ironically) a set of sensors were all connected incorrectly.

Figure 1-10. Whatever can go wrong will go wrong.

When the sensors failed to operate as designed, the parachutes that were to slow down the spacecraft didn't open.

Because of costly failures, designers have installed "fail safes". (*Figure 1-11*) Fail safes are referred to as "idiot proof". But Murphy's Law always seems to strike, even when precautions have been put in place; resulting in "Grave's Law", which states, if you make something idiot proof, the world will create a better idiot".

So what can we learn from this in relation to Human Factors? We can use Murphy's Law as a tool, if we expect things to go wrong and put maintenance safety culture into action, just like Murphy's sled team, a good safety record can be maintained.

Figure 1-11. Fail safes are designed to be "idiot proof".

CONCLUSION

Within this book, the many aspects of human factors are discussed in relation to aviation maintenance. (*Figure 1-12*) The most common of which are introduced along with ways to mitigate the risk to stop them from developing into a problem.

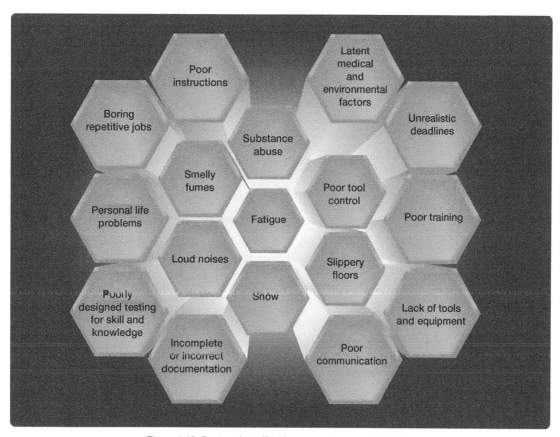
Figure 1-12. Factors that affect human performance for AMTs.

Question: 1-1
What does the "E" in PEAR Model stand for?

Question: 1-2
Because of costly failures, designers have installed
_____, this is referred to "Idiot Proof".

Question: 1-3
Who supposedly stated "If there are two ways to do something, and one will result in disaster, he'll do it that way."?

Question: 1-4
Reduction in near vision is a sign of aging that is anticipated in all AMTs over _____ years of age.

Question: 1-5
What ever can go wrong, will go wrong refers to
_____?

Question: 1-6
Corporate culture of get the job done at all costs would fit which Dirty Dozen factor?

ANSWERS

Answer: 1-1

Environment.

Answer: 1-2

Fail Safes have been installed to protect from costly failures.

Answer: 1-3

Captain Edward A. Murphy, Jr. an Air Force engineer, who Murphy's Law is attributed to.

Answer: 1-4

All AMTs experience reduction in near vision by the age of 50.

Answer: 1-5

Murphy's Law.

Answer: 1-6

The Dirty Dozen factor of getting the job done at all costs is Pressure.

HUMAN FACTORS

HUMAN PERFORMANCE AND LIMITATIONS

SUB-MODULE 02

PART-66 SYLLABUS **LEVELS**

CERTIFICATION CATEGORY →

	B1	B2

Sub-Module 02

HUMAN PERFORMANCE AND LIMITATIONS

Knowledge Requirements

9.2 - Human Performance and Limitations

	B1	B2
Vision;		
Hearing;		
Information processing;	2	2
Attention and perception;		
Memory;		
Claustrophobia and physical access.		

9.2 - HUMAN PERFORMANCE AND LIMITATIONS

INTRODUCTION

This chapter provides an overview of physical and mental human performance factors which affect an Aircraft Maintenance Technicians (AMTs) working environment, such as vision, hearing, information processing, attention and perception, memory, judgment and decision making.

Just as certain mechanical components used in aircraft maintenance have limitations, technicians themselves have certain capabilities and limitations that must be considered when looking at the maintenance 'system'. For instance, rivets used to attach aluminum skin to a fuselage can withstand forces that act to pull them apart. It is clear that these rivets will eventually fail if enough force is applied to them. While the precise range of human capabilities and limitations might not be as well defined as the performance range of mechanical or electrical components, the same principles apply in that human performance is likely to degrade and eventually 'fail' under certain conditions (e.g. stress).

Mechanical components in aircraft can, on occasion, suffer catastrophic failures. People can also fail to function properly in certain situations. Physically, humans become fatigued, are affected by cold, can break bones in workplace accidents, etc. Mentally, humans can make errors, have limited perceptual powers, can exhibit poor judgment due to lack of skills and knowledge, etc. In addition, unlike mechanical components, human performance is also affected by social and emotional factors. Therefore, failure of AMTs can also be to the detriment of aviation safety.

VISION

Vision is vital for AMTs. Think of how much is subject to visual inspection. Vision is best when ensuring appropriate lighting to illuminate the work area, and best protected by ensuring that protective eyewear is clear and suitable for use. An individual's lack of color discrimination, or defective color vision, may make it difficult to distinguish between red and green, even with appropriate illumination. This can lead to errors in tasks such as dealing with electrical wiring.

In order to understand vision, it is useful first to know a little about the anatomy of the eye. (*Figure 2-1*) The basic structure of the eye is similar to a simple camera with an aperture (the iris), a lens, and a light sensitive surface (the retina). Light enters the eye through the cornea, then passes through the iris and the lens, and finally falls on the retina. Here the light stimulates the sensitive cells on the retina (rods and cones) which then pass small electrical impulses by way of the optic nerve to the visual cortex in the brain. Here, the electrical impulses are interpreted and an image is perceived.

BASIC COMPONENTS OF THE EYE

The Cornea

The cornea is a clear 'window' at the very front of the eye. The cornea acts as a fixed focusing device. Focusing is achieved by the shape of the cornea bending the incoming light rays. The cornea is responsible for between 70% and 80% of the total focusing ability (refraction) of the eye.

The Iris and Pupil

The iris (the colored part of the eye) controls the amount of light that is allowed to enter the eye. It does this by varying the size of the pupil (the dark area in the center of the iris). The size of the pupil can be changed very rapidly to cater to changing light levels. The amount of light can be adjusted by a factor of 5:1.

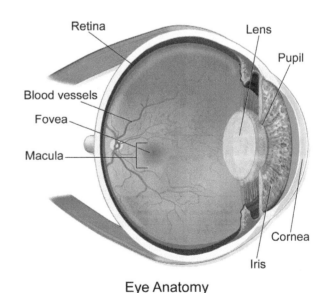

Eye Anatomy

Figure 2-1. The human eye.

The Lens

After passing through the pupil, the light passes through the lens. Its shape is changed by the muscles (ciliary muscles) surrounding it which results in the final focusing adjustment to place a sharp image onto the retina. The change of shape of the lens is called accommodation. In order to focus clearly on a near object, the lens is thickened. To focus on a distant point, the lens is flattened. The degree of accommodation can be affected by factors such as fatigue or the aging process.

When a person is tired, accommodation is reduced, resulting in less sharp vision (sharpness of vision is known as visual acuity).

The Retina:

The retina is located on the rear wall of the eyeball. It is made up of a complex layer of nerve cells connected to the optic nerve. Two types of light sensitive cells are found in the retina; rods and cones. The central area of the retina is known as the fovea and the receptors in this area are called cones. It is here that the visual image is focused. Moving outwards, the cones become less dense and are progressively replaced by rods, so that in the periphery of the retina there are only rods. Cones function in good light, are capable of detecting fine detail, and are color sensitive. This means the human eye can distinguish about 1 000 different shades of color. Rods cannot detect color. They are poor at distinguishing fine detail, but good at detecting movement in the edge of the visual field (peripheral vision). They are much more sensitive at lower light levels.

As light decreases, the sensing task is passed from the cones to the rods. This means in poor light levels we see only in black and white and shades of grey.

Factors Affecting Clarity of Sight

The eye is very sensitive in the right conditions (e.g. clear air, good light, etc.). In fact, the eye has approximately 1.2 million nerve cells leading from the retinas to the area of the brain responsible for vision. As a comparison, there are only about 50 000 nerve cells from the inner ears, making the eye about 24 times more sensitive than the ear.

Before considering factors that can influence and limit the performance of the eye, it is necessary to describe visual acuity. Visual acuity is the ability of the eye to discriminate sharp detail at varying distances. An individual with an acuity of 20/20 vision should be able to see at 20 feet that which the so called "normal" person is capable of seeing at this range. It may be expressed in meters as 6/6 vision. The figures 20/40 mean that the observer can read at 20 feet what a "normal" person can read at 40 feet.

Various factors can affect and limit the visual acuity of the eye such as:
- Physical imperfections in one or both eyes (near sightedness, far sightedness) and age.
- The influence of ingested foreign substances; drugs, medication, alcohol and cigarettes.
- Environmental factors; the amount of light available, clarity of the air (e.g. dust, mist, rain, etc.).
- Other factors associated with object being viewed such as:
  - Size and contours of the object;
  - Contrast of the object with its surroundings;
  - Relative motion of the object;
  - Distance of the object from the viewer;
  - The angle of the object from the viewer.

Blind Spot

Blind spots occurs at the point where the optic nerve enters the retina (between the rods & cones). At the point at which the optic nerve joins the back of the eye, a 'blind spot' occurs. This is not evident when viewing things with both eyes (binocular vision), since it is not possible for the image of an object to fall on the blind spots of both eyes at the same time. Even when viewing with one eye (monocular vision), the constant rapid movement of the eye (saccades) means that the image will not fall on the blind spot all the time. It is only when viewing a stimulus that appears very fleetingly (e.g. a light flashing), that the blind spot may result in something not being seen. Facial features such as the nose also contribute to this problem.

Hold this picture away. Close your left eye and focus on the cross with the right eye. Move the page slowly to the face and at some point the circle shall disappear...the blind spot. (*Figure 2-2*)

AIRCRAFT TECHNICAL BOOK COMPANY

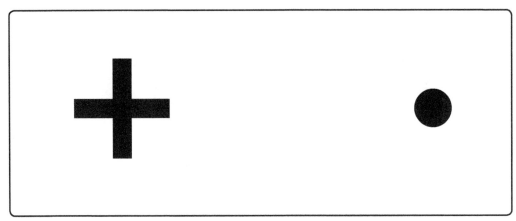

Figure 2-2. Standard test for the "blind spot".

Refractive Errors

Hyperopia (farsightedness) also known as Hypermetropia is caused by a shorter than normal eyeball which means that the image is formed behind the retina. (***Figure 2-3***) If the cornea and the lens cannot use their combined focusing ability to compensate for this, blurred vision will result when looking at close objects. A convex lens overcomes far sightedness by bending light inwards before it reaches the cornea.

Myopia (nearsightedness) is where the eyeball is longer than normal, causing the image to be formed in front of the retina. (***Figure 2-4***) If the accommodation of the lens cannot counteract this then distant objects are blurred. A concave lens overcomes nearsightedness by bending light outwards before it reaches the cornea.

Other visual problems include

- *Cataracts* - clouding of the lens usually associated with aging;
- *Astigmatism* - a misshapen cornea causing objects to appear irregularly shaped;
- *Glaucoma* - a buildup in pressure of the fluid within the eye which can cause damage to the optic nerve and even blindness;
- *Migraine* - severe headaches that can cause visual disturbances.

Foreign Substances

Vision can be adversely affected by the use of certain drugs and medications, alcohol, and smoking cigarettes. With smoking, carbon monoxide which builds up in the bloodstream allows less oxygen to be carried in the blood to the eyes. This is known as hypoxia and can impair rapidly the sensitivity of the rods. Alcohol can have similar effects, even hours after the last drink.

Environmental Factors

Vision can be improved by increasing the lighting level, but only up to a point, as the law of diminishing returns operates. Also, increased illumination could result in increased glare. Older people are more affected by the

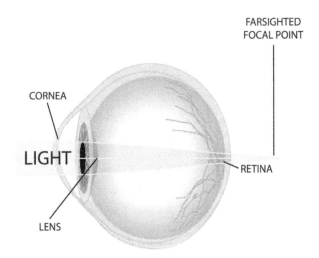

Figure 2-3. Farsighted focus.

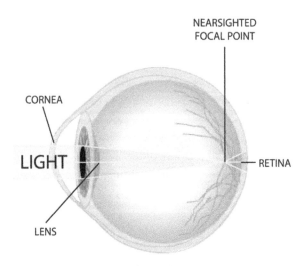

Figure 2-4. Nearsighted focus.

glare of reflected light than younger people. Moving from an extremely bright environment to a dimmer one has the effect of vision being severely reduced until the eyes get used to less light being available. This is because the eyes have become light adapted. If a technician works in a very dark environment for a long time, his eyes gradually become dark adapted allowing better visual acuity. This can take about 7 minutes for the cones and 30 minutes for the rods. As a consequence, moving from a bright hangar (or the inside of a lighted aircraft cabin) to a dark apron area at night can mean that the AMT must wait for the eyes to adjust (adapt). In low light conditions, it is easier to focus if you look slightly to one side of an object. This allows the image to fall outside the fovea and onto the part of the retina that has many rods.

Any airborne particles such as dust, rain or mist can interfere with the transmission of light through the air, distorting what is seen. This can be even worse when glasses are worn, as they are susceptible to getting dirty, wet, misted up, or scratched. AMTs who wear contact lenses (especially hard or gas permeable types) respect the advice from their optician associated with the maximum wear time (usually 8 to 12 hours) and consider the effects which extended wear may have on the eyes, such as drying out and irritation. This is particularly important if they are working in an environment which is excessively dry or dusty, as airborne particles may also affect contact lens wear. Goggles should be worn where necessary.

The Nature of the Object Being Viewed

Many factors associated with the object being viewed can also influence vision. We use information from the objects we are looking at to help distinguish what we are seeing. These are known as visual cues. Visual cues often refer to the comparison of objects of known size to unknown objects. An example of this is that we associate small objects with being further away. Similarly, if an object does not stand out well from its background (i.e. it has poor contrast with its surroundings), it is harder to distinguish its edges and hence its shape. Movement and relative motion of an object, as well as distance and angle of the object from the viewer, can all increase visual demands.

Color Vision

Although not directly affecting visual acuity, inability to see particular colors can be a problem. Among other things, good color vision is needed for recognizing components, distinguishing between wires, using various diagnostic tools; and ability to recognize lights on the airfield (e.g. warning lights).

Color defective vision is usually hereditary, although it may also occur as a temporary condition after a serious illness. Color defective vision (often referred to incorrectly as color blindness, 'Daltonism') affects about 8% of men but only 0.5% of women. The most common type is difficulty in distinguishing between red and green. Less common is the inability to distinguish blues and yellows. (*Figure 2-5*)

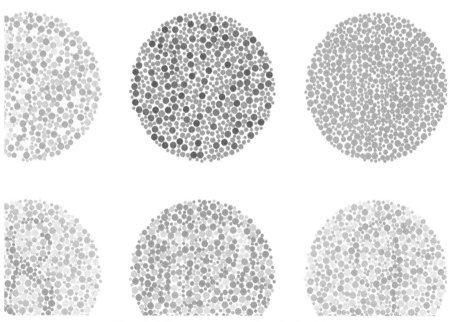

Figure 2-5. Common forms of color defective vision.

There are degrees of color defective vision. Some people suffer more than others. Individuals may be able to distinguish between red and green in a well lit situation but not in low light conditions. People with color defective vision typically see the colors they have problems with as shades of neutral grey. Aging also causes changes in color vision. This is a result of progressive yellowing of the lens, resulting in a reduction in color discrimination in the blue yellow range.

Night Vision and Color Loss

At night or in dim light, central vision can be poor. Better results are obtained by looking slightly to one side of the object rather than directly at them. This permits better use of peripheral vision by using rods instead of the central cones. This effect can be demonstrated by counting a group of faint lights in the distance when looking directly at them; then by looking some 10 degrees to one side, it will be possible to see more lights. Some people who have perfect day vision may be myopic (nearsighted) at night. Night myopia is little recognized but can present a significant hazard, particularly because of the false confidence instilled from having good vision by day.

The reason for night myopia lies in the differing frequency of colors that prevail by night, and the varying ability of the eye's lens to focus them. Red and orange predominate by day. A lens, whether natural or artificial, which is easily capable of focusing these wavelengths can have issues when it tries to focus the more violet colors that prevail at night. In dim conditions the lens has enough elasticity to focus the light from near objects (thus near sightedness) but cannot focus properly on objects further away.

VISION AND THE AGING EYES

A major signpost in the aging process starts at about age 35 years when most individuals first notice difficulty reading fine print. For mechanics, their loss of near vision impacts their job performance.

Accommodation is the subconscious process that allows the lens of the eye to focus light on the retina. This process changes in a predictable pattern with age. Prior to age 35 years focusing between near and far object presents no problem. Starting at age 35, objects held further away are easier to see. Presbyopia, meaning old eyes, is the medical term for this loss of accommodation.

A review of the anatomy of the eye and an understanding of refraction, provide an explanation for presbyopia.

The lens focuses light images onto the retina, the structure with the visually active rod and cone cells. Light from far objects, generally at more than 20 feet away, requires less refraction than light from near objects. For far vision, the lens is in the relaxed condition. Refracting of light by the relaxed lens places a sharp image on the retina *(Figure 2-3)*.

Near vision requires more refraction of light than far vision. Contraction of the ciliary muscles changes the shape of the lens providing the additional refractive power. *(Figure 2-4)*

Starting in the teenage years the lens loses it elasticity but the effect is not noticeable until the early 40s. With this loss of elasticity, the ciliary muscles become less effective in changing the shape of the lens. The refractive capability of the lens declines. Diopter (D) is the unit of measure related to the near point of focus. Accommodation, measured in D as integers and decimals, shows a linear decline until about age 52 years when all accommodation is lost. *(Figure 2-6)*

Aging Eyes Symptoms

Clinical symptoms of presbyopia often start with a difficulty seeing fine print. Over the counter reading glasses starting at +1 D help for a short time. These lenses bend the light coming from near objects to supplement the eye's refractive power. As presbyopia worsens, near vision requires more refractive power so readers with up to +3.25 D are commonly available. Eventually, everything inside of 20 feet looks blurred with the unaided eye. Prescriptions recommended by optometrists include spectacles that contain bifocal, trifocal or progressive lens designs. Other common symptoms are discomfort during reading and a noticeable delay in focusing when changing between distant and near objects.

Why is presbyopia a human factors concern? Consider visual inspection of the aircraft. For good inspection it is assumed a trained inspector has good visual acuity. This assumption may be incorrect considering the aging workforce. With the average AMT age of 53 years in the US, 58 years in Australia, and 45 years in Europe, *Figure 2-6* shows that accommodation is completely lost at these ages.

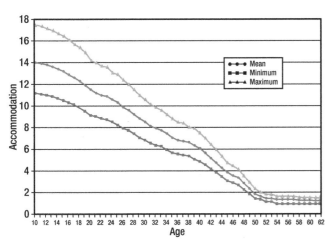

Figure 2-6. Numerical values of maximum, minimum, and mean diopter of accommodation by age. (Ref: Clinical Neuro-Ophthalmology)

Will prescription spectacles or over the counter readers reverse the effects of presbyopia for older mechanics who inspect aircraft? While both offer additional refractive power, the wearer must recognize their zones of vision. *Figure 2-7* shows the zones of vision for five common lens designs used as correction for presbyopia. For each lens design, this figure shows the areas of fixed focal vision. Those wearing bifocals will note a line of discontinuity producing changes in the image. For other designs, the optical performance produces blending of near and far vision. In other words, readers and prescription spectacles can compensate for loss of accommodation but wearers must be knowledgeable which zones of vision will place the image in sharp focus. Head and eye movement may be necessary to ensure clear vision of the work under inspection.

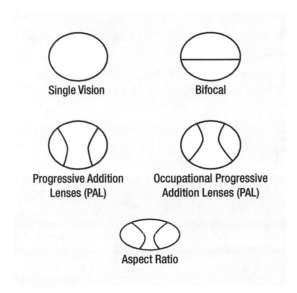

Figure 2-7. Zones of fixed focus vision for different designs of lenses commonly prescribed to correct for presbyopia.

What can be done?

The first step is a risk assessment of those work processes that require careful visual inspections. Common considerations involve the trade off between speed and accuracy of the inspection process. From this assessment the manager can determine the potential risk from presbyopia.

Education of the employees, especially mechanics over the age of 52 years, provides awareness training to those most likely affected by presbyopia.

Aging affects a variety of health conditions, including the severity of chronic disease and impact of on the job injuries. Presbyopia is the age related loss of near vision that can hinder the inspection process. Since this condition can influence safety of flight, identifying its risk through the Safety Management System (SMS) is appropriate.

HEARING

Continuous exposure to high levels of noise can be very fatiguing. It affects cognitive tasks such as memory recall (*"I can't think straight for all that noise!"*). Whenever possible, you should try to lessen or eliminate the source of noise rather than attempting to reduce it by such things as wearing ear protection.

For example, think about closing the hangar doors to remove external sources of noise. However, if you cannot prevent the noise, ensure that appropriate Personal Protective Equipment (PPE) is used. In noisy environments, use appropriate communication headsets where possible, bearing in mind that ear plugs and headsets may restrict you from hearing warnings from other team members, or of approaching hazards. If you are wearing headsets or ear protectors, exercise caution and pay attention.

Colds, flu and ear infections can also affect our hearing capability. Generally, we have poor control over noises in our environment, (we can close our eyes, but cannot close our ears). Use communication equipment (such as headsets) in noisy environments. Moving the aircraft to a more appropriate work area to avoid tarmac noise is an option. Continued exposure to very loud noise leads to fatigue and therefore higher potential for error.

BASIC FUNCTION OF THE EAR

The ear performs two quite different functions. It is used to detect sounds by receiving vibrations in the air, and secondly it is responsible for balance and sensing acceleration. Of these two, the hearing aspect is more pertinent to the AMTs job, and thus it is necessary to have a basic appreciation of how the ear works. As can be seen in *Figure 2-8*, the ear has three divisions: outer ear, middle ear and inner ear. These act to receive vibrations from the air and turn these signals into nerve impulses that the brain can recognize as sounds.

Outer Ear

The outer part of the ear directs sounds down the auditory canal, and on to the eardrum. The sound waves will cause the eardrum to vibrate.

Middle Ear

Beyond the eardrum is the middle ear which transmits vibrations from the eardrum by way of three small bones known as the Ossicles, to the fluid of the inner ear. The middle ear also contains two muscles which help to protect the ear from sounds above 80 dB by means of the acoustic or aural reflex, which can reduce the noise level by up to 20 dB. However, this protection can only be provided for a maximum of about 15 minutes, and does not provide protection against sudden impulse noise such as gunfire. It does explain why a person is temporarily 'deafened' for a few seconds after a sudden loud noise. The middle ear is usually filled with air which is refreshed by way of the eustachian tube which connects this part of the ear with the back of the nose and mouth. However, this tube can also allow mucus to travel to the middle ear which can build up, interfering with normal hearing.

Inner Ear

Unlike the middle ear, the inner ear is filled with fluid. The last of the ossicles in the middle ear is connected to the cochlea, which contains a fine membrane (the basilar membrane) covered in hair like cells which are sensitive to movement in the fluid. Any vibrations they detect cause neural impulses to be transmitted to the brain via the auditory nerve. The amount of vibration detected in the cochlea depends on the volume and pitch of the original sound.

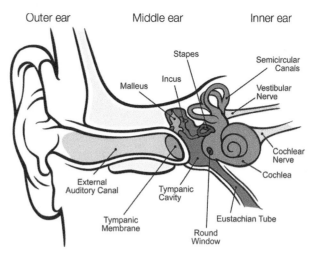

Figure 2-8. The human ear.

PERFORMANCE AND LIMITATIONS OF THE EAR

The performance of the ear is associated with the range of sounds that can be heard - both in terms of the pitch (frequency), and the volume of the sound. The audible frequency range that a young person can hear is typically between 20 and 20 000 cycles per second (or Hertz), with greatest sensitivity at about 3 000 Hz. Volume (or intensity) of sound is measured in decibels (dB).

Impact of Noise on Performance

Noise can have various negative effects in the workplace. It can be some of the following:

- Be annoying (e.g. sudden sounds, constant loud sound, etc.)
- Interfere with verbal communication between individuals in the workplace
- Cause accidents by masking warning signals or messages
- Be fatiguing and affect concentration, decision making, etc.
- Damage workers' hearing (Either temporarily or permanently)

Table 2-1 shows intensity levels for various sounds and activities.

Activity and Distance	Approximate Intensity Level (Decibels)
Rustling of Leaves/Whisper	20
Conversation at 2m	50
Typewriter at 1m	65
Car at 15m	70
Truck at 15m	75

Activity and Distance	Approximate Intensity Level (Decibels)
Power Mower at 2m	90
Propeller Aircraft at 300m	100
Jet Aircraft at 300m	110
Standing near a Propeller Aircraft	120
Threshold of Pain	140
Immediate Hearing Damage Results	150

Table 2-1. Typical sound levels for various activities.

Intermittent and sudden noise is generally considered to be more disruptive than continuous noise at the same level. In addition, high frequency noise generally has a more adverse affect on performance than lower frequency. Noise tends to increase errors and variability, rather than directly affect work rate.

High and Low Tone Deafness

The normal human ear is sensitive to frequencies between about 20 Hz and 20 000 Hz, being particularly sensitive in the range 1 000 Hz to 4 000 Hz and progressively less sensitive at higher and lower frequencies. This is very important when measuring noise since two sounds of equal intensity, but of different frequency, may appear subjectively to be of different loudness.

In the cochlea there are 23 000 nerve cells and each has about 100 sensory hairs (*Figure 2-9*) These hairs sense the vibration of the ossicles. There are two sizes of hair; long; which detect low frequencies, and short; which detect high frequencies. Deterioration of the sensory hairs occurs with over exposure to high levels of noise.

Hearing Protection

Hearing protection is available, to a certain extent, by using ear plugs or ear defenders.

Noise levels can be reduced (attenuated) by up to 20 dB using ear plugs and 40 dB using ear muffs. However, using ear protection will tend to adversely interfere with verbal communication. Despite this, it must be used consistently and as instructed to be effective. As stated before if you are wearing headsets or ear protectors, exercise caution and pay attention.

It is good practice to reduce noise levels at source, or move noise away from workers. Often this is not a practical option. Hearing protection should always be

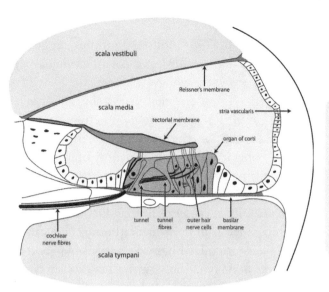

Figure 2-9. Cochlear fibers and nerve cells help detect low and high frequencies.

used for noise, of any duration, above 115 dB. Referring again to *Table 2-1*, this means that you will almost always need to use some form of hearing protection when in reasonably close proximity (about 600–1 000ft or 200–300m) to aircraft whose engines are running.

 *Presbycusis*, the natural reduction in hearing is considered a signpost of aging. However, this assumption does not match the medical observation. Not everyone loses hearing sensitivity with age. Presbycusis can cause hearing loss but so can exposure from noise, solvents, and fuels. Protection of an individual's hearing is a common goal for most hazard based health and safety programs. The goal of a Human Factors (HF) Health and Safety (H&S) program is aviation safety.

While the goals appear different, both recognize the importance of exposures in the workplace. (*Table 2-2*)

Goals for Health and Safety (H&S) Programs with Different Orientations	
Work Hazard Oriented	Personal health protections such as hearing conservation, fall protection, chemical safety.
Human Factors Oriented	Prevent the formation of LMEC that compromise air safety by increasing the risk of a maintenance error.

Table 2-2. Goals for Health and Safety programs with different orientations.

AIRCRAFT TECHNICAL BOOK COMPANY

Two industrial studies suggest that hearing loss is not an inevitable part of the aging workforce. The first, a study of firemen in Pittsburgh, showed a strong correlation between time spent on the job and hearing loss in the "severe" category. The second, a study of a professional automobile race team, showed intermittent exposures to noise as well as fuels, solvents, and other chemicals which are known causes of hearing loss. In both studies the average levels of noise and airborne chemicals were below their recognized hazardous levels but short term exposures occurred. These workplace exposures rather than presbycusis are the major cause of hearing loss in older workers.

These same conclusions were echoed in an FAA Human Factors report on the site evaluation of 23 heavy maintenance environments during 1989 to 1990. The noise levels were below those requiring ear protection but short periods occurred with high noise exposures. The FAA observed numerous instances where the operator's health and safety programs required wearing of safety equipment, such as hearing protection, but the requirement was not enforced in practice.

Based on these studies it is estimated that 20% of the AMT workforce has evidence of a significant hearing loss. This level of hearing loss serves as a starting point for a self assessment of how hearing loss can lead to maintenance errors. To sharpen the estimate, the Safety Management System (SMS) can use known risk factors obtained from the H&S program to more accurately identify those AMTs likely to have a hearing impairment. (*Table 2-3*)

Risk Factors for an LMEC from Hearing Loss
Workers aged over 55 years (four times more likely to demonstrate a hearing loss than workers less that 25 years of age)
Employees with long tenure working in aviation

Table 2-3. Risk Factors for an LMEC from Hearing Loss.

Development of an Hearing &Safety program requires a prioritized set of activities that will limit the potential for miscommunication during maintenance activities.

Hearing conservation activities in a hazard oriented H&S program limit individual's exposures as defined in safety regulations.

Table 2-4 presents examples of activities for both programs. While information from both programs are of value to a Safety Management System (SMS), human factors programs provide more detailed insight into the formation of an Latent Medical and Environmental Condition (LMEC).

Hazard Based Health & Safety Program Compared to Activities for a Human Factors Oriented Program	
HUMAN FACTORS	HAZARD
Assure all AMTs have a basic level of hearing.	Noise monitoring of work area.
Limit conflicting noise in work areas that require team efforts.	Annual audiogram for overexposed AMTs.
Establish commands familiar to all AMTs.	Employee notification.
Match work assignments to personnel with known hearing loss.	Record keeping.

Table 2-4. Activities appropriate for a hazard based health & safety program compared to activities for a human factors oriented program.

Communication with the AMT is required when implementing any H&S program. As the FAA Human Factors showed, this communication must be backed up with management support. For example, if hearing protection is to be worn during line maintenance or solvents are to be uncapped when in the hangar, then supervisors must enforce these requirements.

The assumption that old age causes hearing loss is false. A better assumption is that the SMS can use information from an H&S program that will limit adverse effects of poor hearing.

INFORMATION PROCESSING

Information processing is the process of receiving information through the senses, analyzing, and making it meaningful. We make many decisions every day. To do this, we need to have a look at the ways in which we process information.

INFORMATION PROCESSING MODEL

Human beings basically process information in five stages. (*Figure 2-10*)

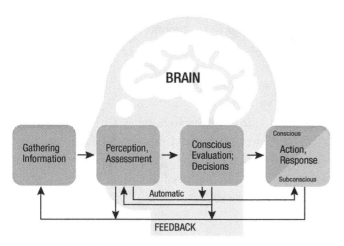

BRAIN

Figure 2-10. The stages of information processing.

Stage 1: Gathering Information

First we must gather information. We do this by using our senses (sight, hearing, touch or smell), to collect information using receptors, which transform this information (about temperature, for example) into sensations (feels hot). Stimuli can either originate from an external source such as sound, or from an internal one, such as thirst or hunger.

Stage 2: Perception or Assessment

Once we have gathered this information, we must make sense of it. This involves perception and assessment, arguably the most important stage in the whole process. Our brain gives the information an initial review to see whether it is meaningful; for example, have we seen this before? At this point we must satisfy our human need to understand our environment. To do so we rapidly create an internal model (like a pattern) with which we are comfortable. The resulting model or pattern is influenced in two ways: by the raw sensory information we perceive; and either by previous experience, or our current expectations.

Here is where we are most vulnerable to being fooled either by the information itself, or by our own expectations; meaning our own eagerness to make the input fit what we have seen before. So, depending on our interpretation, our brain takes preliminary steps to work out how the information is to be dealt with. If our brain has seen it all before and it is commonplace; for example, walking up a flight of stairs, or changing gears while driving the car; the information is directed via the automatic (or motor) program path. If the information is new or complex, our brain assigns it to the full conscious evaluation/decision route.

Stage 3: Evaluation and Decision Making

If the information is complex or new, our brains will deal with it by giving it full and conscious attention. We may make the decision immediately or store the information for a later decision. This will require the use of memory. Our initial evaluation may show that the input is familiar, so we can deal with it using a well known procedure or method that has worked before; for example, putting a nut on a bolt. Doing so will still require a small amount of our conscious attention, but for the most part our response is directed automatically.

On the other hand, our initial evaluation might be that this new information is complex or unfamiliar. When this occurs, we have to think more deeply to resolve the situation. Quite often this will require such a level of concentration and brainpower that our ability to attend to other matters will be reduced, or even disappear. An example is trying to understand a previously unknown electrical wiring fault, or dealing with an unfamiliar engine running emergency.

Stage 4: Action/Response

Our action or response occurs either consciously, with full awareness, or subconsciously using our automatic programs. If it is performed consciously, we act and/or speak with full attention. If it is performed subconsciously, we act as if we are on 'automatic pilot'.

Visualize an automatic task you can perform while doing other things; for example, driving a car while maintaining a conversation. But if the driving task becomes more difficult, such as attempting to parallel park in a particularly tight spot, our brain will revert to the 100 percent full attention requirement, and we stop our conversation. So while we can do more than one thing at a time, our brain is limited by being able to process only one thing at a time!

Stage 5: Feedback

The final stage is feedback, which allows us to confirm that what we are getting is what we are expecting. Feedback is not just a one time event. It occurs continuously throughout the various stages of information processing to ensure the information we are receiving continues to fit our expectations. The feedback stage provides the opportunity for:

• Clarifying details of the information.
• If need be, seeking out additional information.
• Refining the information.
• Making small or large corrections with our actions and/or responses.
• Identifying emerging hazards.

The whole process is repeated as often as necessary, so that either the status quo is retained, or necessary changes are implemented. When performing any skilled task like opening the cowling to check fluids, we continuously monitor both the environment and the consequences of our action to form a closed loop feedback system. This provides us with valuable opportunities to assess both emerging errors and hazards. Identifying errors in a timely manner means that corrections can be made, and ensures the action continues as intended. In the fluid check, we must be sure that we checked fluids, but also have properly closed the cowling.

However, in the maintenance workplace, incorrect actions may not give instant feedback–under torqued bolts, or omitted locking devices (split pins etc.), may not provide feedback for months after the error.

AMTs should have a basic awareness and understanding of how individuals process information. This helps us to better understand and accept error in ourselves and in others. This understanding of information processing is particularly useful when analyzing errors, as it helps us to determine whether they are the consequence of one, or a combination of the following:

• Deficiencies in receiving stimuli/information through our senses (not enough information).
• Deficiencies in perception/assessment of the information (not deciphering the information accurately).
• Deficiencies in the evaluation and decision making processes.
• Inappropriate action/response, despite satisfactory processing to that point.

• Failure to monitor or respond to the feedback properly.
• Effect of external factors detrimental to the process overall, such as excessive workload or fatigue.

High workload, and periods with a high volume of information to be processed in a short time frame, can cause information overload. This may lead to degraded performance and an increased likelihood of error. This is why checklists are so important.

ATTENTION AND PERCEPTION

ATTENTION

Having detected information, our mental resources are concentrated on specific elements–this is attention. Attention can be thought of as the concentration of mental effort on sensory or mental events. Although attention can move very quickly from one item to another, it can only deal with one item at a time. Attention can take the form of:

• *Selective Attention:* occurs when a person is monitoring several sources of input, with greater attention being given to one or more sources which appear more important. A person can be consciously attending to one source while still sampling other sources in the background. Psychologists refer to this as the 'cocktail party effect' whereby you can be engrossed in a conversation with one person but your attention is temporarily diverted if you overhear your name being mentioned at the other side of the room, even though you were not aware of listening in to other people's conversations.
• *Distraction:* the negative side of selective attention.
• *Divided Attention:* common in most work situations, where people are required to do more than one thing at the same time. Usually, one task suffers at the expense of the other, more so if they are similar in nature. This type of situation is also sometimes referred to as time sharing.

- *Focused Attention:* the skill of focusing one's attention upon a single source and avoiding distraction.
- *Sustained Attention:* the ability to maintain attention and remain alert over long periods of time, often on one task.

Attention is influenced by arousal level and stress. This can improve attention or damage it, depending on the circumstances.

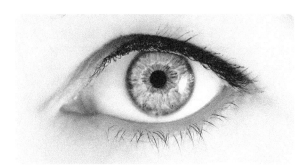

PERCEPTION

Perception involves the organization and interpretation of sensory data in order to make it meaningful, discarding irrelevant data. Perception is a highly sophisticated mechanism and requires existing knowledge and experience to know what data to keep and what to discard, and how to associate the data in a meaningful manner.

Perception can be defined as the process of assembling sensations into a usable mental representation of the world. Perception creates faces, melodies, works of art, illusions, etc., out of the raw material of sensation.

Examples of the perceptual process:
- The image formed on the retina is inverted and two dimensional, yet we see the world the right way up and in three dimensions.
- If the head is turned, the eyes detect a constantly changing pattern of images, yet we perceive things around us to have a set location, rather than move chaotically.

Having recognized coherent information from the stimuli reaching our senses, a course of action has to be decided upon. In other words, decision making occurs. Decision making is the generation of alternative courses of action based on available information, knowledge, prior experience, expectation, context, goals, etc., and selecting one preferred option. It is also described as thinking, problem solving and judgment.

This may range from deciding to do nothing, to deciding to act immediately in a very specific manner. A fire alarm bell, for instance, may trigger a well trained sequence of actions without further thought. Alternatively, an unfamiliar siren may require further information to be gathered before an appropriate course of action can be initiated.

Finally, once a decision has been made, an appropriate action can be carried out. Our senses receive feedback of this and its result. This helps to improve knowledge and refine future judgment by learning from experience.

If a task is performed often enough, it may eventually become automatic and the required skills and actions are stored in long term memory. These are known as motor programs and are ingrained routines that have been established through practice. The use of a motor program reduces the load on the central decision maker. An often quoted example is that of driving a car: at first, each individual action such as shifting is demanding, but eventually the separate actions are combined into a motor program and can be performed with little or no awareness.

These motor programs allow us to carry out simultaneous activities, such as having a conversation while driving. Although not shown explicitly in *Figure 2-10*, the process of attention, perception and judgment should result in awareness of the current situation.

Illusions of Perception
There are many well known visual 'illusions' which illustrate the limits of human perception. *Figure 2-11* shows how the perceptual system can be misled into believing that one line is longer than the other, even though a ruler will confirm that they are exactly the same. *Figure 2-12* illustrates that we can perceive the same thing quite differently (i.e. the letter "B" or the number "13"). This shows the influence of context on our information processing.

It is often necessary to consult documents with which the technician can become very familiar. It is possible that to scan a document and fail to notice that subtle changes have been made. You will only see what you expect to see. To illustrate how our eyes can deceive us when quickly scanning a sentence, read quickly the sentence in *Figure 2-13*.

At first, most people tend to notice nothing wrong with the sentence. Our perceptual system subconsciously rejects the additional "A".

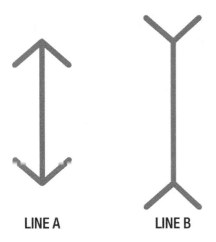

LINE A   LINE B

Figure 2-11. The Muller-Lyer Illusion.

Figure 2-12. An example of perception.

Figure 2-13. The effects of expectation.

As an illustration of how expectation can affect our judgment, the same video of a car accident was shown to two groups of subjects. One group was told in advance that they were to be shown a video of a car crash; the other was told that the car had been involved in a 'bump'. Both groups were asked to judge the speed at which the vehicles had collided. The first group assessed the speed as significantly higher than the second group.

Expectation can also affect our memory of events. The study outlined above was extended such that subjects were asked, a week later, whether they recalled seeing glass on the road after the collision. (There was no glass). The group, who had been told that they would see a crash, recalled seeing glass; the other group recalled seeing no glass.

Attention and perception shortcomings can clearly affect decision making. Perceiving something incorrectly may mean that an incorrect decision is made, resulting in an inappropriate action. *Figure 2-13* also shows the dependence on memory to make decisions. Sensory and short term memories have limited capacity, both in terms of capacity and duration. It is also important to bear in mind that human memory is fallible, so that information:

- May not be stored;
- May be stored incorrectly;
- May be difficult to retrieve.

The points above can be referred to as forgetting, which occurs when information is unavailable (not stored in the first place) or inaccessible (cannot be retrieved). Information in short term memory is particularly susceptible to interference, an example of which would be trying to remember a part number while trying to recall a telephone number.

Maintenance personnel must use manuals and temporary aides rather than to rely upon memory, even in circumstances where the information to be remembered or recalled is relatively simple. For instance, an AMT may remember a torque setting without writing it down, but between consulting the manual and walking to the aircraft (possibly stopping to talk to someone on the way), may forget the setting or confuse it (possibly with a different torque setting appropriate to a similar task with which he is more familiar). Additionally, if unsure of the accuracy of memorized information, you should seek to check, even if this means going elsewhere to do so. Writing something down temporarily can avoid the risk of forgetting or confusing information. However, the use of a personal note book to capture such information on a permanent basis can be dangerous, as the information in it may become out of date.

Situation Awareness

Situation awareness is the synthesis of an accurate and up to date 'mental model' of one's environment and state, and the ability to use this to make predictions of possible future states. Situation awareness has traditionally been used in the context of the flight deck to describe the pilot's awareness of what is going on; for example, where are we geographically, what is our orientation in space, what mode is the aircraft in, etc.

In the maintenance technician's context, it refers to:
- The perception of important elements, for example, seeing loose bolts, missing parts, leaking fluids, and hearing information passed verbally.
- The comprehension of their meaning, for example, why is it like this? Is this how it should be?
- The projection of their status into the future, for example, future effects on safety, schedule, and airworthiness.

Situation awareness for an AMT can be summarized as:
- The status of the system that is being worked on.
- The relationship between the reported defect and the intended rectification.
- The possible effect on this work on other systems.
- The effect of this work on that being done by others and the effect of their work on this work.

A proportion of 'sensed' data may be lost without being 'perceived'. An example with which most people are familiar is that of failing to perceive something which someone has said to you, when you are concentrating on something else, even though the words would have been received by the ear without any problem. The other side of the coin is the ability of the information processing system to perceive something (such as a picture, sentence, concept, etc.) even though some of the data may be missing. The danger however, is that people can fill in the gaps with information from their own store of knowledge or experience, and this may lead to the wrong conclusion being drawn.

Once we have formed a mental model of a situation, we often seek information which will confirm this model and, not consciously, reject information which suggests that this model is incorrect.

MEMORY

Memory is critical to our ability to act consistently and to learn new things. Without memory, we could not capture a 'stream' of information reaching our senses, or draw on past experience and apply this knowledge when making decisions.

MEMORY PROCESS

Registration   Storage   Retrieval

MEMORY PROCESSES

Memory can be considered to be the storage and retention of information, experiences and knowledge, as well as the ability to retrieve this information.
Memory depends on three processes:
- *Registration* - the input of information into memory;
- *Storage* - the retention of information;
- *Retrieval* - the recovery of stored information.

It is possible to distinguish between three forms of memory. (*Figure 2-14*)
- *Ultra Short Term* (or sensory storage), has a duration of up to 2 seconds (depending on the sense) and is used as a buffer, giving us time to attend to sensory input.
- *Short Term* (often referred to as working memory), receives a proportion of the information received into sensory stores, and allows us to store information long enough to use it (hence the idea of 'working memory'). It can store only a relatively small amount of information at one time, often 7+/- items of information. As the following example shows, capacity of short term memory can be enhanced by splitting information in to 'chunks' (a group of related items).

A telephone number, e.g. 03035551212, can be stored as 11 discrete digits, in which case it is unlikely to be remembered. Alternatively, it can be stored in chunks of related information, e.g. in the US, 303 may be stored as one chunk, 555 as another, and 1212 as another,

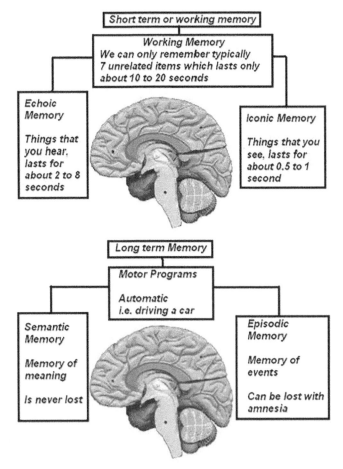

Figure 2-14. Differences between long and short term memory.

using only 3 chunks and therefore, more likely to be remembered. In mainland Europe, the same telephone number would probably be stored as 03 03 55 51 21 2, using 6 chunks. The size of the chunk will be determined by the individual's familiarity with the information (based on prior experience and context). A person from the UK might recognize 0208 as the code for London, but a person from mainland Europe might not.

The duration of short term memory can be extended through rehearsal (mental repetition of the information) or encoding the information in some meaningful manner (e.g. associating it with something as in the example above).

- *Long Term*. The capacity of long term memory appears to be unlimited. It is used to store information that is not currently being used, including: knowledge of the physical world and objects within it and how these behave; personal experiences; beliefs about people, social norms, and values; motor programs, problem solving skills and plans for achieving various activities; abilities such as language comprehension.

Information in long term memory can be divided into two types.

- *Semantic Memory* refers to our store of general, factual knowledge about the world, such as concepts, rules, one's own language, etc. It is information that is not tied to where and when the knowledge was originally acquired.
- *Episodic Memory* refers to memory of specific events, such as our past experiences (including people, events and objects). We can usually place these things within a certain context. It is believed that episodic memory is heavily influenced by a person's expectations of what should have happened, thus two people's recollection of the same event can differ.

CLAUSTROPHOBIA AND PHYSICAL ACCESS

 Claustrophobia can be defined as abnormal fear of being in an enclosed space. There are many circumstances where people may experience various levels of physical or psychological discomfort when in an enclosed or small space. This is generally considered to be quite normal. When this discomfort becomes extreme, it is known as claustrophobia.

It is quite possible that susceptibility to claustrophobia is not apparent at the start of employment. It may come about for the first time because of an incident when working within a confined space, e.g. panic if unable to extricate oneself from a fuel tank. If one suffers an attack of claustrophobia, they should make coworkers and supervisors aware so that if tasks likely to generate claustrophobia cannot be avoided, at least coworkers may be able to assist in extricating from the confined space quickly, and sympathetically.

Team work will help in assisting one another if necessary, making allowances for the fact that people come in all shapes and sizes and that it may be easier for one person to access a space, than another.

FEAR OF HEIGHTS

Working at significant heights can also be a problem, especially when doing 'crown' inspections (top of fuselage, etc.). Some may be quite at ease in situations like these, whereas others may be so uncomfortable that they are far more concerned about the height, and holding on to the access equipment than they are about the job in hand.

In such situations, it is very important that appropriate use is made of harnesses and safety ropes. These will not necessarily remove the fear of heights, but will certainly help to reassure the technician to concentrate on the task in hand. If one finds working high up brings on phobic symptoms (such as severe anxiety and panic), they should avoid such situations for safety's sake. However, as with claustrophobia, support from team members can be helpful.

Shortly before the Aloha Airlines accident, an inspector needed ropes attached to the rafters of the hangar to prevent falling from the aircraft when it was necessary to inspect rivet lines on top of the fuselage. Although unavoidable, this would not have been conducive to ensuring that the inspection was carried out meticulously (nor was it, as the subsequent accident investigation revealed). The National Transportation Safety Board (NTSB) investigation report stated:

> *"Inspection of the rivets required inspectors to climb on scaffolding and move along the upper fuselage carrying a bright light with them. In the case of an eddy current inspection, the inspectors needed a probe, a meter, and a light. At times, the inspector needed ropes attached to the rafters of the hangar to prevent falling from the airplane when it was necessary to inspect rivet lines on top of the fuselage. Even if the temperatures were comfortable and the lighting was good, the task of examining the area around one rivet after another for signs of minute cracks while standing on scaffolding or on top of the fuselage is very tedious. After examining more and more rivets and finding no cracks, it is natural to begin to expect that cracks will not be found."*

One of the many functions of the supervisors should be an attempt to make the job as comfortable and secure as reasonably possible (e.g. providing knee pad rests, ensuring that staging does not wobble, providing ventilation in enclosed spaces, etc.) and allow for frequent breaks.

CONCLUSION

The technician is the key component to the aircraft maintenance system. It is imperative to have a useful understanding of how different parts of the body and mental processes function, and understand how our brain and perceptions may be "tricked". With this awareness and with proper accommodations, mistakes leading to accidents can be avoided.

Question: 2-1
The retina is located on what part of the eyeball?

Question: 2-2
What facial feature can contribute to the blind spot?

Question: 2-3
What shape lens would be used for nearsightedness?

Question: 2-4
The most common type of color blindness "Daltonism" is the difficulty distinguishing between what two colors?

Question: 2-5
At night, best results for vision can be achieved looking which way at an object?

Question: 2-6
Presbycusis is the natural reduction in _____?

Question: 2-7
The information processing involves what five stages?

Question: 2-8
What are the three processes of Memory?

ANSWERS

Answer: 2-1

The retina is located on the rear of the eyeball.

Answer: 2-2

The nose can block the field of vision and contribute to the blind spot.

Answer: 2-3

A concave lens. It helps compensate by bending light outwards before it reaches the cornea.

Answer: 2-4

There are many forms of color defective vision, but the most common form is distinguishing between red and green.

Answer: 2-5

Best results can be achieved by looking to one side of an object.

Answer: 2-6

Presbycusis is the natural reduction in hearing.

Answer: 2-7

Information processing involves:
1. Gathering Information
2. Perception or Assessment
3. Evaluation and Decision Making
4. Action/Response
5. Feedback

Answer: 2-8

The three processes of memory are:
1. Registration
2. Storage
3. Retrieval

HUMAN FACTORS

SOCIAL PSYCHOLOGY

SUB-MODULE 03

PART-66 SYLLABUS LEVELS

	CERTIFICATION CATEGORY →	B1	B2

Sub-Module 03

SOCIAL PSYCHOLOGY

Knowledge Requirements

9.3 – Social Psychology

	B1	B2
Responsibility: individual and group; Motivation and demotivation; Peer pressure; "Culture" issues; Team working; Management, supervision and leadership.	1	1

9.3 - SOCIAL PSYCHOLOGY

INTRODUCTION

The vast majority of Aircraft Maintenance Technicians (AMTs) work for a company, either directly or as a contract employee. It is important to understand how the organization might influence the employee as every company has different ways of operating. This is what we call organizational culture. Every company has its own philosophy, policies, procedures, training criteria, and quality assurance methods.

RESPONSIBILITY
(INDIVIDUAL AND GROUP)

Personal standards include how one treats themselves, how they treat others, how they behave in front of others, and how they perform their jobs at the highest level. Who we are, how we are raised, and how we are taught influences our personal standards. During training, new employees will adopt the behaviors of the more experienced people who mentor them. Instilling qualities of professionalism and responsibility in the early stages of training is important so they can become the foundation of the individual's attitudes and behaviors in the workplace.

All tasks require attention to detail, as well as adherence to duty and procedures to ensure they are done accurately. Occasionally one may be challenged by normal behaviors also called "norms", where methods used have become the accepted practice at the workplace. "I did it this way because this is how it is always done around here." AMTs need to recognize this behavior and decide if the task is being performed as safety requires, or as it "normally gets done". This is where personal standards become important.

Would you certify a job on behalf of another AMT you hardly knew, who had completed a task that you were responsible for, if you had not inspected the work performed?

This dilemma is more common than you would imagine. Often an AMT will be overseeing multiple tasks on different areas of an aircraft and may even at the same time be involved and responsible for other aircraft. He or she may have to certify that all this simultaneous work has been performed in accordance with approved standards.

Personal integrity should thus empower the AMT to check that the work is done correctly while combining the promotion of safety, integrity, professionalism, and above all else, a resistance to risky behavior.

Case Study: Taking it For Granted
During the reactivation of a thrust reverse mechanism after maintenance, an experienced AMT reactivating the Center Drive Unit (CDU) lockout needed a suitable platform to visually inspect the upper locking mechanism of the cowling reverser halves. As he left the task, another AMT who had recently joined the team offered to complete the reactivation of the drive unit.

Returning to the engine with the required platform, the senior AMT observed the engine's final cowlings being closed by the AMT with the help of another AMT who had been working on the opposite engine. The senior AMT asked the newer AMT if the CDUs were returned to flight condition. The newer AMT informed the senior AMT that the task was complete and that they just needed to latch the final sets of engine cowls (which was observed).

When it came time to complete the maintenance documentation, an entry for the thrust reverser lockout had to be cleared. The newer AMT had already left the aircraft to clean up, and as it was nearing the end of the late shift, the senior AMT signed for the task being completed in accordance with the aircraft maintenance manual. His belief was that the task had been completed competently without actually checking the CDUs as the other technicians were closing the engine. So they could ready the aircraft, he left it in a serviceable and a released to service condition.

The next morning, when landing in gusty wind conditions on a shorter than normal runway, full thrust reverse was applied and the affected engine did not respond accordingly. As a precaution, and to avoid asymmetric reverse thrust which could lead to loss of control, both engines were selected to forward thrust, and maximum wheel braking applied. As a result of this action seven of the eight wheel brakes needed to be replaced before the next flight.

An investigation into the maintenance activities from the evening before revealed that the newer AMT had never performed the reactivation of the CDU task before and only observed the senior technician removing the lock plate bolts. Not fully aware of why this action was being performed, the newer AMT thought the bolts were being fitted, not removed, and therefore required tightening. This action left the lockout plate fitted with the drive lock inserted, thus mechanically deactivating the thrust reverser.

Key Lessons
All personnel involved in the task must be fully aware of its progress. This vigilance is an important part of professional behavior. Good communication can avoid the potential for taking things for granted making risky decisions. Assuming is not a sign of professional behavior.
- Never sign for work you have not performed, especially if you have not inspected or observed it personally.
- Trust should not replace good communication and proper vigilance. Again, if you did not do or inspect the work, you should not sign for it.

Key Points
- Professionalism comprises those attitudes and behaviors that place the interests of safety above one's own self interest.
- Professionalism can be developed in isolated one person operations, as well in as larger organizations with a number of technicians.
- Professionalism is a characteristic that can both drive (and be driven by), the safety culture of an organization.
- Colleagues and mentors have a strong influence on professionalism, from the earliest days of a technician's career.

GROUP OR TEAM RESPONSIBILITY

Group responsibility has both its advantages and disadvantages. The advantages are that each member of the group ought to feel responsible for the output of that group, not just their own output as an individual. Each member must work together towards ensuring that the whole 'product' is safe. This may involve cross checking others' work (even when not strictly required), politely challenging others if you think that something is not quite right, etc.

The disadvantage of group responsibility is that it can potentially act against safety, with responsibility being diluted to such an extent that no one feels personally responsible. Often while an individual on his own may take action; once placed within a group, may not act if none of the other group members do so. Each member of the group or team often just assumes that 'someone else will do it'.

Social psychologists have carried out experiments, contriving a situation in which someone was apparently in distress, and noting who came to help. If a person was on their own, they were far more likely to help than if they were in a pair or group. In the group situation, each person felt that it was not solely their responsibility to act and assumed that someone else would do so.

Here are some other recognized phenomena associated with team working and responsibility which AMTs should also be aware of.

Intergroup conflicts involve situations where a small group may act cohesively as a team, but less so between teams. (e.g. between technicians and planners, between shifts, between teams at different sites, etc). This may have implications in terms of responsibility, with different teams failing to share responsibility between themselves. This is particularly pertinent during shift handovers, where members of the outgoing shift may not feel responsible for waiting for the incoming shift to arrive; thus bypassing a verbal handover in support of the written task sheets. Each might feel such responsibility when handing over tasks within their team but not between teams.

Group Polarization/Groupthink

Group Polarization (Groupthink) is the tendency for groups to make decisions that are more extreme than the individual members' initial positions. At times, group polarization results in more cautious decisions. Alternatively in other situations, a group may arrive at a course of action that is riskier than that which any individual member might pursue. This is known as a risky shift.

Another example of group polarization is Groupthink in which the desire of the group to reach unanimous agreement overrides any individual impulse to adopt a more rational or responsible procedure.

Social Loafing

Social Loafing has been coined to reflect the tendency for some individuals to work less hard on a task when they believe others are working on it. In other words, they consider that their own efforts will be pooled with that of other group members and not seen in isolation.

MOTIVATION AND DEMOTIVATION

MOTIVATION

Motivated behavior is goal directed, purposeful behavior. No human behavior occurs without some kind of motivation behind it. In aircraft maintenance, technicians are trained to carry out the tasks within their expertise. However, it is largely their motivation which determines what they actually do in any given situation. Thus, "motivation reflects the difference between what someone can do and what they will do".

Motivation can be thought of as a basic human drive that arouses, directs, and sustains all human behavior. Generally we say a person is motivated if they take action to achieve something. Motivation is usually considered to be a positive rather than a negative force in that it stimulates one to achieve various things. However, just because someone is motivated, they still might not do the right thing. Many criminals are highly motivated.

Motivation is difficult to measure and predict. We are all motivated by different things, an artist might strive over many months to complete a painting that will never be sold, and a person in business may forfeit all family life in pursuit of financial success. A mechanic might be motivated to complete a task, for which he or she is not qualified. With respect to safety, being motivated is vital. AMTs ought to be motivated to work safely and efficiently. However, many factors may conflict with this ideal.

For instance, the motivation of some financial bonus, or demotivation of working outdoors in extreme cold might lead to less consideration of safety and an increase in the likelihood of risk taking, corner cutting, violating procedures and so on.
- External and Internal Motivation
    - External: System rewards & punishments
    - Internal: Do it because we want to
- What people want from work
    - To feel valued and competent
    - To feel in control

Internal motivation (doing things because you want to rather than because someone else has told you to) is far more effective than external sticks and carrots. Punishing (or rewarding inappropriately) people who are internally motivated can be counter productive.

Reward and Punishment: Effects on Behavior
Figure 3-1 summarizes what psychologists know about the effects of reward and punishment in the workplace. Rewards are the most powerful means of changing behavior, but they are only effective if delivered close in time and place to the behavior that is desired. Delayed punishments have negative effects: they don't lead to improved behavior and they make people resentful.

	IMMEDIATE	DELAYED
Reward	Positive Effects	Doubtful Effects
Punishment	Doubtful Effects	Negative Effects

Figure 3-1. The effects of punishment and reward on behavior.

The cells labeled 'doubtful effects' mean that, in each case, there are opposing forces at work. Hence, the results are uncertain.

Maslow's Hierarchy of Needs
One well known theory which attempts to describe human motivation is Maslow's hierarchy of needs. Maslow considered that humans are driven by two different sets of motivational forces;
- ...those that ensure survival by satisfying basic physical and psychological needs.
- ...those that help us to realize our full potential in life known as self actualization needs (fulfilling ambitions, etc.).

Figure 3-2 shows the hypothetical hierarchical nature of the needs we are motivated to satisfy. The theory is that the needs which are lower down the pyramid are more primitive and must be satisfied before we can be motivated by the higher needs. For instance, you will probably find it harder to concentrate on the information in this document if you are very hungry (as the lower level physiological need to eat predominates over the

Figure 3-2. Maslow's pyramid—the higher up you go on the pyramid the more difficult it becomes to satisfy the need.

higher level cognitive need for self esteem). The higher up the pyramid one goes, the more difficult it becomes to achieve the need. High level needs are often long term goals that have to be accomplished in a series of steps.

An interesting experiment on motivation was carried out in 1924 at the Hawthorne Works of the Western Electric Company in Chicago. Here, the management altered various factors such as rest periods, lighting levels, working hours, etc. Each time they did so performance improved, even when the apparent improvements were taken away! This suggested that it was not the improvements themselves which were causing the increased production rates, but rather the fact that the employees felt that management were taking notice of them and were concerned for their welfare. This phenomenon is known as the Hawthorne effect.

"*The Hawthorne Effect* (also referred to as the **observer effect**) is a type of reactivity in which individuals modify or improve an aspect of their behavior in response to their awareness of being observed." (*Figure 3-3*)

DEMOTIVATION

Highly motivated people tend to show the following characteristics:
  • High performance and results being consistently achieved.
  • The energy, enthusiasm and determination to succeed.
  • Unstinting cooperation in overcoming problems.
  • Willingness to accept responsibility.
  • Willingness to accommodate change.

People who are demotivated lack motivation, either internally or through a failure of their management to motivate them. Demotivated people tend to demonstrate the following characteristics:

Figure 3-3. Workers perform better when they believe they are being observed.

  • Apathy and indifference to the job, including reduced regard for safety while working.
  • A poor record of time keeping and high absenteeism.
  • An exaggeration of the effects/difficulties encountered in problems, disputes and grievances.
  • A lack of cooperation in dealing with problems or difficulties.
  • Unjustified resistance to change.

The motivating effects of job security and the demotivating impact of lack of job security is an area that causes much debate. The 'hire and fire' attitude of some companies can potentially be a major influence on safety, with real or perceived pressure upon individuals affecting their performance and actions.

It is important that AMTs are motivated by a desire to ensure safety (Maslow's self esteem/self respect'), rather than by a fear of being punished and losing their job (Maslow's 'security'). It is possible that the "can do" culture, which is evident in some areas of the industry, may be generated by the expectancy that if individuals do not 'deliver', they will be punished and, conversely, those who do 'deliver' (whether by the book or not, finding ways around lack of time, spares, or equipment) are rewarded and promoted.

PEER PRESSURE
In the working environment of aircraft maintenance, there are many pressures brought to bear on the individual technician, including the possibility that he/she will receive personal pressures from those that work with them. This is known as peer pressure.

Peer pressure is the actual or perceived pressure which an individual may feel, to better conform to what they perceive that their peers or colleagues expect.

For example, an individual may feel that there is pressure to cut corners in order to get an aircraft out by a certain time, including the belief that their colleagues would do such under similar circumstances. There may be no actual pressure from management to cut corners, but instead subtle pressure from peers. For example, a comment such as "You don't want to bother checking the manual for that. Just do it like this..." would constitute peer pressure.

Peer pressure thus falls within the area of conformity. Conformity is the tendency to allow one's opinions, attitudes, actions and even perceptions to be affected by prevailing opinions, attitudes, actions and perceptions. Peer pressure is the pressure we feel to do what our group or peers expect of us. Peer pressure is closely linked to organizational norms and culture. As with organizational culture, peer pressure or conformity can work either for, or against safety.

An organization with a positive safety culture, for example, will exert pressure on newcomers to operate with a professional and positive attitude. However, an organization in which shortcuts and non compliance are commonplace will have a negative influence on the behavior of individuals. If individuals are expected to cut corners to get the job done, peer pressure can influence others to do the same.

Solomon Asch carried out several experiments investigating the nature of conformity, in which he asked people to judge which of lines A, B & C was the same length as Target Line. (*Figure 3-4*)

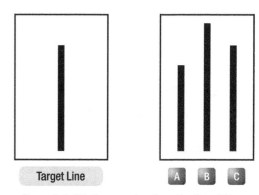

Figure 3-4. C is the same length as the Target Line.

He asked this question under different conditions:
- The individual was asked to make the judgment on their own.
- The individual carried out the task after a group of 7–9 others had all stated that line A was the correct choice.

Of course, the real participant did not know the others were "stooges".

EXPERIMENT TO ILLUSTRATE CONFORMITY (SOLOMAN ASCH-1951)

In the first condition, very few mistakes were made (as would be expected of such a simple task with an obvious answer). In the latter condition, on average, participants gave wrong answers on one third of the trials by agreeing with the accomplices. Clearly, participants yielded to group pressure and agreed with the incorrect 'group' finding (however, it is worth mentioning that there were considerable individual differences, some participants never conformed, while others conformed all the time).

The degree to which an individual's view is likely to be affected by conformity or peer pressure, depends on many factors, including:
- Culture (people from country 'x' tend to conform more than those from country 'y').
- Gender (men tend to conform less than women);
- Self-esteem (a person with low self esteem is likely to conform more).
- Familiarity of the subject matter (a person is more likely to conform to the majority view if they know less about the subject matter).
- The expertise of the group members (if the individual respects the group or perceives them to be very knowledgeable he or she will be more likely to conform to their views).

AIRCRAFT TECHNICAL BOOK COMPANY

The relationship between the individual and group members (conformity increases if the individual knows the other members of the group, i.e., it's a group of peers).

CULTURE ISSUES

Safety culture basically involves the attitudes coworkers hold about the company's approach to safety, their perceptions of the magnitude of the risks, and their belief in the necessity, practicality and effectiveness of measures to control risk. In this way, safety culture can be considered an enabler for safety. Safety culture is made up of those shared beliefs, values, and practices affecting the safety of the environment. Think about how culture affects the way one thinks and acts.

HOW DOES THE ORGANIZATIONAL CULTURE AFFECT THE WORK OF AN AMT?

In the working environment, safe and professional practices are not only expected normal behavior, but are reinforced and supported by management (even when under considerable pressure to get the aircraft serviceable and on line). In this type of culture, personnel will tend to 'do it by the book' and take the time to ensure the appropriate work, inspections, and signoffs are actually carried out. If, however, one works in a culture where shortcuts and workarounds are commonplace or where 'near enough is good enough', even those with good intentions can be drawn into these norms and begin to accept lower and lower standards.

THE INFLUENCE OF ORGANIZATIONAL CULTURE ON SAFETY

Continental Express Flight 2574 was a scheduled domestic passenger flight operated by British Airways from Laredo, Texas to Houston, Texas. On September 11, 1991, the Embraer EMB-120 crashed as it was approaching the runway to land, killing all 14 people onboard. The US National Transportation Safety Board

(NTSB) investigation revealed bolts had been removed from the horizontal stabilizer during maintenance the night before the accident and, following a shift change, the bolts were not replaced. The plane crashed on its second flight of the day.

The NTSB cited the failure of airline maintenance and inspection personnel to adhere to proper maintenance and quality assurance procedures.

The failure of Federal Aviation Administration (FAA) surveillance to detect and verify compliance with approved procedures was cited as a contributing factor. Following the accident, the FAA conducted a National Aviation Safety Inspection Program (NASIP) of Continental Express's maintenance program. It found very few safety deficiencies, and complimented the airline on its internal evaluation system. However, the NTSB expressed concern that the NASIP had not found deficiencies in shift turnover procedures and other relevant matters, and recommended that the agency improve its procedures. The NTSB determined the probable causes of this accident as follows:

> "The failure of maintenance and inspection personnel to adhere to proper maintenance and quality assurance procedures for the aircraft's horizontal stabilizer deice boots. This led to the sudden inflight loss of the partially secured left horizontal stabilizer leading edge, and the immediate severe nose down pitch over and breakup of the aircraft. A contributing cause of the accident was the failure of management to ensure compliance with the approved maintenance procedures. In addition, the failure of FAA surveillance to detect and verify compliance with approved procedures was cited."

Role in Developing the Culture of Safety

As a member of the National Transportation Safety Board (NTSB) at that time, Dr. John Lauber suggested that the probable cause of this accident included 'the failure of Continental Express management to establish a corporate culture which encouraged and enforced adherence to approved maintenance and quality assurance procedures'.

Adapted from NTSB report on Continental Express flight 2574 accident, 11 September 1991.

AIRCRAFT
TECHNICAL
BOOK COMPANY

How do you recognize an organization with a good safety culture?

An organization with a good safety culture is one where safe and professional behavior is fully internalized as the way personnel think and act. It is one where safety is seen as a required outcome of all operations, and where safe and professional practices are not only endorsed by management, but are proactively demonstrated. We are not simply talking about the number of safety posters around the workspace, but a realistic demonstration of support for safe and professional operations at all levels of the organization. In a safe culture each worker can define their specific role in safety.

Sometimes, due to commercial pressures to get the aircraft out under an unrealistic time schedule, AMTs can be pressured to cut corners; for example, to sign off work that has not actually been checked or carried out strictly according to laid down procedures. Under these circumstances, it is very easy for a poor safety culture to develop, where personnel are rewarded for getting the aircraft out on time, even though everyone knows that corners have been cut to achieve that. In turn, this can rapidly deteriorate into a culture where shortcuts and violations become commonplace and eventually become normal accepted practice within the organization. This culture can be difficult and slow to change.

TEAMWORK

Teams require interdependence; members working together in ways to achieve one or more common goals.

Successful teamwork is achieved when the output of the team is greater than what the output would be by the combined efforts of the individual members in isolation. This is a process known as synergy. Synergy occurs when each individual team member is empowered and encouraged to contribute in the most effective way to the overall task of the team. Interaction between team members creates a positive environment, increasing efficiency and productivity.

This interaction is unlikely to occur unless all members of the team fully understand their role within the group, and how this role might vary depending on circumstances. Consequently, good communications within the group, a high degree of situational awareness, and a comprehensive understanding of the decision making process by all members are prerequisites

Alone we can do so little, together we can do so much.
–Helen Keller

for creating synergy. Sound teamwork in aviation maintenance is also a vital error management tool. There are many examples where maintenance team failures have been found to be major factors in aviation accidents.

CHARACTERISTICS OF TEAMS

Good teams have certain characteristics. Typically, individual team members have high levels of task proficiency and good team skills. So what are the characteristics of teams with good synergy? These teams:
- Share and understand a common goal
- Have effective and balanced leadership
- Have effective followership (or team) skills
- Have a shared mental model
- Practice clear and effective communication
- Have clear delegation/role definition
- Have clear operating procedures
- Allocate workload appropriately
- Have an appropriate authority gradient
- Resolve conflict effectively

CONDITIONS FOR EFFECTIVE TEAMWORK

Shared and Understood Goal
This is closely linked with providing a clear pre task briefing. It is often assumed that everyone in the team knows what the goal is. However, this is not always the case. For a team to be effective, all team members need to know what the specific goal is, as well as what they

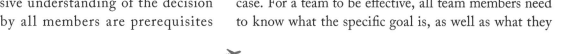

need to do to achieve it. When the team has a shared and understood goal, all members of the team are 'pulling in the same direction' to achieve the stated goal, rather than working in isolation.

Effective Leadership and Followership

Good balanced leadership and followership skills are critical for effective team performance. The team leader needs to manage the workload, keep the team motivated, provide appropriate direction when required, and coordinate activities aimed at achieving the team goal. The follower is expected to act professionally, work towards the team goal and raise issues if they are unsure or disagree.

Effective teamwork will occur when team members have confidence in their leader and are consulted about and involved in making decisions. A good team leader takes the time to listen to and evaluate input from team members and decides the best way to achieve a safe and efficient result; even if this course of action might not have been their first choice.

A Shared Mental Model

For a team to be effective, each member should be aware of the expected outcomes of their work. Supervisors therefore have to communicate what is required, how they expect it to be achieved, and allocate appropriate tasks and responsibilities. The shift or task supervisor should communicate before the team begins the task. It may then require frequent briefing during the task, so the whole team remains aware of, and is focused on what needs to be achieved. Regular briefing and informal discussion with team members during the task should ensure that all team members share the same mental model.

Regular thorough briefings should be carried out at the following times:
- At the beginning of every shift
- When the work priorities change
- When another task is issued
- Whenever important information needs to be communicated

It is very vital throughout, that the maintenance team maintains an understanding of what they are trying to achieve, what processes they will follow in order to achieve it, its current status, along with what should happen next.

Practice Clear and Effective Communication

Individuals develop and coordinate activities to achieve goals by communicating with each other–by exchanging information. Effective communication is a complex process. Some have simplistically summarized the process in these four steps:

1. Someone transmits information.
2. Someone else receives that information.
3. That receiver understands the information, and finally.
4. Confirms to the transmitter that they have received and understood the information.

However, there are numerous places where this communication can break down. 'Someone transmits information' and 'someone else receives that information' sounds quite straightforward, but the person communicating the information may not be using the most appropriate means for their audience. For example, sending information in an email may be effective for one group, but not for others in which a face to face talk would be more appropriate.

The choice of delivery method also depends on what has to be communicated. If it is simply technical information or task instruction, an email or written briefing may be appropriate. However, more sensitive team building or motivational communication will require a more personal face to face delivery where both parties can use visual and verbal cues such as body language to understand how what is being said is also being received.

Adapting the tone and language of your communication to your audience is also vital. For example the language of an academic journal is very different to that of a daily news bulletin. Academic journals are more formal and are often written in more technical language for a narrow specialist audience. The daily news bulletin needs to be written in accessible plain English in order to reach as broad an audience as possible.

For maintenance teams to work effectively, anyone passing on information to the team needs to ensure that the individual team members understand the meaning and context of what is being conveyed.

Regular effective communication is vital to forming and maintaining a shared mental model and ensuring everyone is on the same page. Good communication is also necessary for maintaining a high level of situational awareness. Having high levels of situational awareness will help teams to be more effective.

Clear Delegation & Role Definition

There must be a clear outline of who is responsible for what. Clear delegation and role definition helps to minimize duplicated effort and ensures that each team member knows what they have to do and who is responsible for what. Delegating responsibilities appropriately within the team, and defining individual team members' roles, ensures activities are coordinated and no one team member is overloaded, thus allowing their ability to assist other team members when necessary. Delegating responsibilities and defining roles also ensure that team members have the capability to monitor each other's performance and provide support as required.

Clear Operating Procedures

Aviation maintenance is highly process driven, however sometimes there is little guidance to the maintenance team on how they should do the job. Having

standardized operating procedures means all members of the maintenance team know what is expected and how a task should be carried out. And also what the other members will be doing in accordance with those procedures. Clear operating procedures are the hallmark of a well organized and efficient organization. They provide a baseline of how personnel will carry out a given procedure and encourage consistency in team performance.

Appropriate Allocation of Workload

We tend to be most reliable under moderate levels of workload that do not change suddenly and unpredictably. When the workload becomes excessive, the likelihood of human error increases. The term 'workload' can be summarized as the task demands placed upon an individual, and the corresponding ability of that individual to cope with those demands. An individual's ability to cope with demands will be affected by their inherent capabilities, training, skill level, tiredness, and a multitude of other factors. This has several implications:

- Different people will experience different workloads for the same task. Remember how difficult it was when you were learning to drive? Changing gears required massive concentration and effort, while experienced drivers can change gear almost without thinking.
- Workload levels will vary as time passes. For example, you will tend to become more fatigued and/or bored as the shift progresses.

High workload and inappropriate/unrealistic time frames in which to achieve tasks can have an adverse effect on team performance. Maintenance teams that experience a consistently high workload, or are confronted with conflicting demands to complete tasks within an unrealistic time frame often use shortcuts and workarounds. Workload, therefore, must be appropriately balanced within the team.

AIRCRAFT TECHNICAL BOOK COMPANY

Appropriate Authority Gradient

Workplace gradients (status/age/experience) may discourage inexperienced personnel from engaging with, or questioning someone who is more experienced or of higher status. Conversely, more experienced personnel, or those of higher rank, may feel they do not need to listen to the views or opinions of those with less experience.

Differences in position, experience and age between members can lead to an inappropriate authority gradient within the team. An inexperienced team member may find it difficult to express their concerns about a decision made by a more experienced supervisor or team member.

Conflict Resolution

Conflict will arise from time to time. It can destroy team cohesion when the argument is over who is right, rather than what is right. Conflict resolution requires assertiveness, a willingness to confront what is often an emotional issue, effective communication skills, and a real desire to resolve the issue. People will not always agree. Differences of opinion, brought out into the open, based on facts, and discussed within the team are healthy and can be a useful part of making and reviewing decisions. Disagreements between team members show that all team members feel that they have a right to express their views and ensure that decisions and alternative courses of action are reviewed. However, you need to manage such disagreements, and deal appropriately with even minor or implied conflict within the team. The key issue in resolving a conflict is first to determine 'what is right?' (the facts) and not necessarily 'who is right?' (the emotions). To achieve this, actively listen to, acknowledge, and try to understand the other's perception of the situation/facts. Don't threaten the feelings or competence of other team members and avoid emotional statements.

KEY POINTS

Safe and efficient maintenance relies on the successful performance of the maintenance team. Successful teamwork is achieved when the output of the team is greater than that which could be achieved by the sum of the efforts of the individual team members acting in isolation.

For a team to be effective all its members need to know the specific goal, as well as what is required to achieve it.

Poor leadership or followership will negatively affect team performance. The team leader needs to manage the workload, keep the team motivated, provide appropriate direction when required, and coordinate activities aimed at achieving the team goal.

For a team to be effective, each member should be aware of the expected outcomes of their work. This can and should be communicated by the shift or task supervisor and may require frequent briefing during a task to ensure that the whole team remains aware of the goals.

Effective communication is vital for teamwork and for situational awareness so that everyone knows who is responsible for what.

Standardized operating procedures allow all members of the maintenance team to know what is expected and also what actions other members will be taking.

When workload is excessive, the likelihood of human error increases.

The key issue in resolving a conflict is to determine the facts: 'what is right?' and not necessarily the emotional 'who is right?'. To achieve this, actively listen to, acknowledge, and try to understand, the other's perception of the situation/facts.

MANAGEMENT, SUPERVISION AND LEADERSHIP

Managers and supervisors have a key role to play in ensuring that work is carried out safely. It is no good instilling the engineers and technicians with 'good safety practice' concepts, if these are not supported by their supervisors and managers.

Unless you are the lead dog, the scenery never changes.

THE MANAGEMENT ROLE

Line Managers, particularly those working as an integral part of the 'front line' operation, may be placed in a situation where they may have to compromise between commercial drivers and 'ideal' safety practices (both of which are passed down from 'top management' in the organization). For example, if there is a temporary staff shortage, he or she must decide whether maintenance tasks can be safely carried out with reduced manpower, or whether an AMT volunteering to work a "back to back shift" will be able to perform adequately. The adoption of Safety Management Principles may help by providing managers with techniques whereby they can carry out a more objective assessment of risk.

THE SUPERVISORY ROLE

Supervision may be a formal role or post (i.e. a supervisor), or an informal arrangement in which a more experienced personnel 'keeps an eye on' less experienced staff. The supervisor is in a position not only to watch out for errors which might be made by technicians, but will also have a good appreciation of individual 's strengths and weaknesses, together with an appreciation of the norms and culture of the group. It is mainly the supervisor's job to prevent unsafe norms from developing, and to ensure that good safety practices are maintained.

There can be a risk however, that the supervisor becomes drawn down the same cultural path as the team without realizing. It is good practice for a supervisor to step back from the day to day work on occasion and try to look at performance objectively.

It can be difficult for supervisory and management staff to strike the right balance between carrying out their supervisory duties and maintaining their own skills and knowledge (and appropriate authorizations), and they may thus get out of practice.

Also, there is unlikely to be anyone monitoring or checking the supervisor, because:
- The supervisor's seniority. Supervisors are generally authorized to sign for their own work.
- They need to step in when there are staff shortages and therefore there is no spare staff to monitor or check their task.
- The supervisor may be more sensitive to any commercial pressures which may exist, or may perceive that pressure to a greater extent than other staff.

LEADERSHIP

Characteristics of a Good Leader
A leader in a given situation is a person whose ideas and actions influence the thought and the behavior of others. There are potentially two types of leader in aircraft maintenance:
1. The person officially assigned the team leader role (possibly called the Supervisor)
2. An individual within a group that the rest of the group tends to follow or defer to (possibly due to a dominant personality, etc.). Ideally of course, the official team leader should also be the person the rest of the group defers to.

What is leadership?

Motivating the Team
The leader organizes the team by ensuring that the goals or targets of the work which need to be achieved are clearly communicated and manageable. For instance,

the team leader would describe the work required on an aircraft within a shift. The leader must be honest and open, highlighting any potential problems and where appropriate encourage team solutions.

Reinforcing Good Attitudes and Behavior

When team members work well (i.e., safely and efficiently), this must be recognized by the team leader and reinforced. This might be by offering a word of thanks for hard work, or making a favorable report to senior management on an individual. A good leader will also make sure that bad habits are eliminated and inappropriate actions are **constructively** criticized.

Demonstrating by Example

One of the most important leadership qualities is setting an example; doing what they say. They must demonstrate a personal understanding of the activities and goals of the team so that the team members respect their authority. It is particularly important that the team leader establishes a good safety culture within a team through attitude and actions.

Maintaining the Group

Individuals do not always work together as good teams. It is part of the leader's role to be sensitive to the structure of the team and the relationships within it. They must engender a 'team spirit' where the team members support each other and feel responsible for the work of the team. They must also recognize and resolve disputes within the team and encourage cooperation amongst its members.

Fulfilling a Management Role

The team leader must not be afraid to lead (and diplomatically making it clear that there cannot be more than one leader in a team). The team leader is the link between higher levels of management within the organization and the team members who actually work on the aircraft. The leader is responsible for coordinating the activities of the team on a day to day basis, which includes allocation of tasks and delegation of duties. There can be a tendency for team members to transfer some of their own responsibilities to the team leader. This must be resisted.

Skilled management, supervision, and leadership play a significant part in the attainment of safety and high quality human performance in aircraft maintenance.

In terms of the relationship between managers, supervisors and technicians, a 'them and us' attitude is not conducive to improving the safety culture of an organization. It is important that managers, supervisors, and technicians all work together rather than against one another to ensure that aircraft maintenance improves airworthiness.

What leadership is not!

- Leadership is not power. The thug who sticks a gun in your back has power, but not leadership.
- Leadership is not status. Some may have status or position, yet do not have a shred of leadership.
- Position is assigned from above ... leadership is conferred from below.
- Leadership is not authority. Bosses will naturally have subordinates, but if bosses do not lead, they will not have followers.
- Leadership is not management. Managing is a planned activity: leadership is more spontaneous.
- Managers do things right. Leaders do the right things.

Management is about making sure people CAN work safely; that is, provide the right tools and equipment, have good policies and procedures, hold safety meetings and training, and so on. Leadership, on the other hand, is about helping to ensure that people WILL work safely: providing consistent feedback to people when they are doing the right kinds of things around safety, make safety meetings engaging and relevant, model safe behaviors in all, make the connection and balance between production, quality, and safety and celebrate successes. As an AMT is chosen to lead other people, challenges soon appear.

Leadership under stress

Aviation maintenance often requires the skills of a good leader in situations that present the individual and team with various challenges. As human beings we have to deal with these challenges in various ways which can sometimes create stressful conditions in which good leadership qualities need to prevail. Having all the available information at the time and communicating with those involved directly and indirectly with the task poses significant challenges to getting the job done.

Consider the following scenario

You are the senior engineer at a maintenance organization that supports an inhouse charter operation consisting of seven 10 seater, twin engine aircraft. One of the aircraft has been chartered to take two mining engineers to a remote airfield two hours away and return. This is the only aircraft available on the day as the others are either in service elsewhere or are in the middle of maintenance checks in the hangar. The pilot who flew this particular aircraft that morning reported the fuel quantity indicator had been not operating properly and that it should be replaced. It is still readable, but some of the bar lights on the digital display are not working properly. A maintenance manual test of the unit confirms this. You then discover a replacement instrument is not in stock. Getting another will take 24–48 hours from an overhaul company. As this aircraft is the only suitable type available and the client is a potentially lucrative source of further business, the operations office asks if there is an alternative to releasing the aircraft in this condition.

Even the chief pilot has offered to operate the flight, despite the fuel quantity indicator not functioning fully, reasoning 'If it's only a couple of lights on the display, it should be okay, because I can still read it'.

Do you weigh up the possible outcomes of releasing the aircraft, while considering the value this client could bring to the flight operations side of your business? Or do you set an example to your team and your employer by insisting the flight does not begin unless a serviceable indicator is installed as per the manufacturer's requirements.

The answer should seem obvious. However, such stressful situations with competing demands and pressures can test our leadership skills.

CONCLUSION

The organizational culture of the workplace has a great impact on the safety practices.

This impact can be both positive and negative. Organizations may encourage their employees (both financially and with other incentives) to take notice of problems the AMT may encounter, and attempt to learn and make changes where necessary. On the negative side the organization may exert pressure on its technicians to get work done within tight time scales and on budget. At times, individuals feel that these conflict with their ability to sustain the quality of their work. Organizational stresses lead to problems with quality, high turnover, increased absenteeism, and more incidents and accidents due to human error.

Within aircraft maintenance, responsibility should be spread across all those who play a part in the activity.

SOCIAL PSYCHOLOGY

Question: 3-1

What is the main advantage of group or team responsibility?

Question: 3-2

What is the definition of social loafing?

Question: 3-3

Name at least five characteristics of highly motivated people.

Question: 3-4

On the bottom of Maslow's Hierarchy of needs, which is the most basic need to satisfy?

Question: 3-5

The best way to affect change in behavior is with immediate or delayed punishment or reward?

Question: 3-6

Name at least five characteristics of good teams?

Question: 3-7

There are two types of leaders; what are they?

Question: 3-8

What is peer pressure?

ANSWERS

Answer: 3-1
Each member of the team feels responsible for the output of the group.

Answer: 3-2
The tendency to put less effort into a task with the belief that others are working on it.

Answer: 3-3
Characteristics of highly motivated people include: high performance; energy; enthusiasm; determination; cooperation; willingness to accept responsibility; willingness to accommodate change.

Answer: 3-4
The most basic needs to satisfy are physiological needs.

Answer: 3-5
The best way to affect change in behavior is with immediate rewards.

Answer: 3-6
Characteristics of good teams include:
shared common goals; effective and balanced leadership; effective followership (or team) skills; a shared mental model; clear and effective communication; clear delegation/role definition; clear operating procedures; allocate workload appropriately; an appropriate authority gradient; resolve conflict effectively.

Answer: 3-7
The person is officially assigned to the team; An individual within a group that the rest of the group follow or defer to.

Answer: 3-8
Peer pressure is when behavior is influenced by friends and colleagues.

HUMAN FACTORS

FACTORS AFFECTING PERFORMANCE

SUB-MODULE 04

Sub-Module 04

FACTORS AFFECTING PERFORMANCE

Knowledge Requirements

9.4 - Factors Affecting Performance
   Fitness/health;
   Stress: domestic and work related;
   Time pressure and deadlines;
   Workload: overload and underload;
   Sleep and fatigue, shiftwork;
   Alcohol, medication, drug abuse.

2   2

FACTORS AFFECTING
PERFORMANCE

9.4 - FACTORS AFFECTING PERFORMANCE

INTRODUCTION

There are many factors that adversely affect an Aircraft Maintenance Technician (AMT). Some of the main human factors include fitness and health, stress, time pressures and deadlines, workload, fatigue, shift work, and the effects of alcohol and drugs. In this chapter we will explore how these factors affect us adversely and can put safety at risk.

FITNESS AND HEALTH

There are two aspects to fitness and health: The disposition of the AMT prior to taking on employment and the day to day well being once employed.

PREEMPLOYMENT PHYSICAL

Some employers may require a medical preemployment physical. This allows the employer to judge the fitness and health of the applicant. There is an obvious effect upon an AMTs ability to perform his or her job if through poor physical fitness or health, the applicant is constrained in some way (such as freedom of movement). In addition, an airworthiness authority when considering issuing a license, will consider these factors and may judge the condition to be of such significance that a license could not be issued.

DAY TO DAY FITNESS AND HEALTH

Fitness and health can have a significant effect upon job performance (both physical and cognitive). Day to day fitness can be reduced through illness (physical or mental) or injury.

EASA Part-66 imposes a requirement that "certifying staff must not exercise the privileges of their certification authorization if they know or suspect that their physical or mental condition renders them unfit".

Responsibility often falls upon the individuals to determine whether or not they are well enough to work on a particular day. Alternatively, team members or supervisors may intervene. Many conditions can impact on the health and fitness of an individual, such as:

- Minor physical illness (such as colds, flu, etc.);
- More significant physical illness (such as cancer, heart conditions, etc.);
- Mental illness (such as depression, anxiety, etc.)
- Minor injury (such as a sprained wrist, etc.)
- Major injury (such as a broken arm, etc.);
- Latent Medical and Environmental Conditions (LMECs) such as ongoing deterioration, possibly associated with the aging such as hearing loss, visual defects, obesity, heart problems, etc.);
- Effects of toxins and other foreign substances (such as carbon monoxide poisoning, alcohol, illicit drugs, etc.).

There is no hard and fast guidelines as to what constitutes 'unfit for work'. This is a complex issue dependent upon the nature of the illness or condition, its effect upon the individual, the type of work to be done, environmental conditions, etc. Instead, it is important that the AMT is aware that his/her performance, and consequently the safety of aircraft he/she works on, might be affected adversely by illness or lack of fitness.

AMTs may consider that they are letting down coworkers by not going to work when ill, especially if there are ongoing manpower shortages. However, management should generally allow for contingency for illness. The burden should not be placed upon an individual to turn up to work when unfit if no such contingency is available. If the individual has a contagious illness such as the flu, other workers become at risk as well.

POSITIVE MEASURES

There are many things AMTs can do to help maintain fitness and health. These include:

- Eating regular meals and a well balanced diet;
- Regular exercise (sufficient to double the resting pulse rate for 20 minutes, three times a week is often recommended);
- Stop smoking;
- Sensible alcohol intake.

STRESS: DOMESTIC AND WORK RELATED

INTRODUCTION

 Stress is the high level of emotional arousal typically associated with an overload of mental and/or physical activity. Stress is often associated with anxiety, fear, fatigue, and hostility. It can also arise as a result of feelings of inadequacy, where we may feel we don't have the appropriate experience, knowledge, or capability to complete our allocated tasks. All these feelings can have a direct and negative impact on performance.

Stress is an inevitable and necessary part of life. It can motivate us and heighten our response to meeting the challenges we face. In fact, our performance will generally improve with the onset of stress, but will peak and then begin to degrade rapidly as stress levels exceed our adaptive abilities to handle the situation.

High levels of stress are a problem for any individual or team, since the effects of stress are often subtle and difficult to assess. Although complex and difficult maintenance activities can generate stress, there is also both physical and mental stress that a team member may bring to the situation and which others may not be able to detect.

CHARACTERISTICS OF STRESS

Stress is often described as being insidious; that is, it develops slowly and has a gradual and cumulative effect. It can be well established before we are aware that it is degrading our performance. We may think that we are handling everything quite well, when in fact there are subtle signs that our performance has degraded to a point where we can no longer respond appropriately.

STRESS IS CUMULATIVE

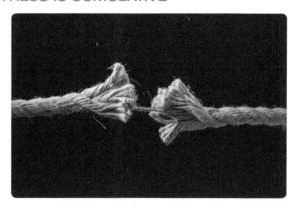

We are all under a certain level of stress at any given time, but there is a limit to any individual's capability to adapt to increasing stress. This stress tolerance level is based on our ability to cope with a given set of circumstances. If the number or intensity of stressors becomes too great, we can become overloaded. At this point, our performance begins to decline and our judgment deteriorates.

CAUSES OF STRESS

Any changes in personal circumstances such as marital separation, bereavement, difficult family affairs, or financial concerns can lead to stress and affect our emotional state. There is also work related stress, which may include real or imagined commercial pressures, such as the need to juggle deadlines to get an aircraft on line, and balance economic considerations with the understanding that lives depend on the quality of our work. To complicate matters even further, admitting to suffering from these stresses is often viewed by coworkers as an admission of weakness or failure. Early symptoms of stress such as depression or sleep disruption are often denied. In this situation we tend to look for other ways to cope with our high levels of stress, such as aggression, drugs or alcohol.

STRESSORS

Different stressors affect different people to varying extents. Typical stressors include:

- Physical, such as heat, cold, noise, or the onset of fatigue;
- Psychological, such as worries about real or imagined problems (e.g. financial problems, ill health, etc.);
- Reactive, such as events occurring in everyday life (e.g. working under unrealistic time pressure, bullying, encountering unexpected situations, etc.).

SYMPTOMS OF STRESS

The symptoms of stress can include:

- Physiological symptoms, such as sweating, dryness of the mouth etc.;
- Health effects, such as nausea, headaches, sleep problems, stomach upsets;
- Behavioral symptoms, such as restlessness, shaking, nervous laughter, taking longer over tasks, changes to appetite, excessive drinking or smoking etc.;
- Cognitive effects, such as poor concentration, indecision, forgetfulness etc.;
- Subjective effects, such as anxiety, irritability, depression, moodiness, aggression etc.

CONSEQUENCES FOR AMTS

Inappropriately high levels of stress can significantly degrade performance and as a result can also compromise safety. Under extreme levels of stress, the following behaviors can be evident:

- Poor judgment;
- Compromised, or accepting of lower standards;
- Inattention, loss of vigilance and alertness;
- Preoccupation with a single task at the expense of others;
- Forgetting or omitting procedural steps;
- Greater tendency towards losing things;
- Misreading maintenance manuals and procedural steps;
- Loss of time perception;
- Loss of situational awareness.

DOMESTIC STRESS

Domestic stress typically results from major life changes such as divorce, the birth of a child, or the death of a family member or close friend. Preoccupation with domestic stress can play on our mind during working hours, distracting us from our tasks. This inability to concentrate fully may affect task performance, error rates and our ability to pay sufficient attention to safety.

WORK RELATED STRESS

Carrying out tasks that are new, or very challenging or difficult, can make us feel stressed. Time pressure, lack of standard procedures or appropriate resources, lack of guidance or supervision, and interpersonal conflicts all intensify this stress. Some of these stressors can be reduced by appropriate workload management, good communication, good training etc. The social and managerial aspects of work can also be stressful; for example if you feel your job is under threat due to a company reorganization.

MANAGING STRESS

If we all work with a certain amount of stress, how can we ensure it is kept to an appropriate level? Recognizing high stress situations such as undergoing divorce, suffering a bereavement; or having an argument with a spouse or boss are worries which can build to an unbearable level. Even with low levels of stress, levels can build; particularly when there is a multitude of decisions to make or tasks to complete. Before this occurs, we need to be proactive in managing the stress load so that it does not become unmanageable. We can control physiological stressors by strategies like:

- Maintaining good physical fitness and bodily function;
- Engaging in a program of regular physical exercise;
- Getting enough sleep to prevent fatigue;
- Eating a balanced diet;
- Learning and practicing relaxation techniques.

We can also reduce the physical stressors by making the work environment as stress free as possible.

In high pressure situations, relieve stress by establishing priorities and by appropriately delegating tasks and responsibilities to other members of the team. In a low pressure situation, where fatigue, boredom and over familiarity with the task are the greatest hazards, paying careful attention to environmental conditions such as heat, humidity, noise, and lighting can help to maintain alertness. You can often reduce mental stressors by making your physical work environment as stress free as possible.

STRESS COPING STRATEGIES

If coping strategies are to be effective, we need to identify and deal with the source of the stress, and not just the symptoms. For example, delegate workload when necessary, appropriately prioritize tasks, and sort out problems rather than letting them fester. We cannot always change the situation–it may be outside our control–but even when this is the case, there are a number of coping strategies we can use.

Achieving Relaxation

There are almost as many techniques, practices, and treatments for dealing with stress as there are causes of it. From ancient relaxation techniques to the latest thinking on proper nutrition; from breathing exercises to repetitive prayer, there are numerous tools to help people cope. Some techniques can be especially beneficial under certain circumstances but not as helpful under others.

Understanding what works for us as individuals and for the stressful circumstances at hand can require an exploration of a number of stress reduction methods. And as always, it is important to know when to seek professional help. These efforts can reward you richly with better health, greater peace of mind, and a smoother course through life.

How stressed are you?

This quick quiz may make you more aware of the impact of significant life events on your level of stress. The following table lists a number of life events the average person could expect to experience. To test yourself, just go through the list and add up the points of the events you have experienced in the last year. Add the points allocated to each of these events in the right hand column to find your total cumulative score. (*Table 4-1, Page 4.6*)

What Your Score Means

Each of us has personal stress adaption limitations. When we exceed this level, stress overload may lead to poor health or illness. Although different people have different capacities to cope with stress, for the average person a score of 250 points or more may indicate that you are suffering from high levels of stress.

Studies revealed that people who had become ill had accumulated a total of 300 stress points or more in a single year. Look at the last twelve months of changes in your life. It is important to understand that 'ripples of stress' can circulate a long time after the actual change has taken place. High stress levels will adversely affect your immune system and lead to mental or physical illness if something is not done. It is very important to lighten the stress load and develop mechanisms to cope with stress before something happens. The message for AMTs is clear. If stress brought on by life changes is not managed well, and is added to the stresses in the workplace, performance will be adversely affected.

TIME PRESSURE AND DEADLINES

TIME PRESSURE AND SELF IMPOSED PRESSURE

There are two types of pressure; actual pressure and self imposed pressure. The first is real pressure, applied directly or indirectly, for the task to be completed in a given time. On the other hand, individuals or teams may feel self imposed pressure to complete a task within a given time, even when the time available may be unrealistic or the task may not be achievable with the allocated resources and time frame.

For an individual, the self imposed pressure is real. For them it is no different from any actual pressure being applied to the completion of the task. All pressure (self imposed or otherwise) will affect the performance of those subjected to it. Inappropriate pressure applied to an individual or maintenance team to achieve a task is a safety risk. Actual and self imposed pressure can be significant drivers for error and taking maintenance short cuts.

How can inappropriate actual or self imposed pressure be managed?

- Allocate appropriate time for all maintenance tasks
- Carry out a comprehensive pretask briefing to outline the task priorities;
- Ensure open two way communication to identify and mitigate the effects of pressure on performance and behavior.

Communicating any problems encountered during the task is vital, particularly when you cannot complete the task safely because of insufficient time and resources.

AIRCRAFT TECHNICAL BOOK COMPANY

Life Event	Score	Cumulative Score
Death of spouse.	100	
Divorce.	60	
Menopause.	60	
Separation from living partner.	60	
Jail term or probation.	60	
Death of close family member other than spouse.	60	
Serious personal injury or illness.	45	
Marriage or establishing life partnership.	45	
Fired from work.	45	
Marital or relationship reconciliation.	40	
Retirement.	40	
Change in health of immediate family member.	40	
Work more than 40 hours per week.	35	
Pregnancy or partner becoming pregnant.	35	
Sexual difficulties.	35	
Gain of new family member.	35	
Business or work role change.	35	
Change in financial state.	35	
Death of a close friend (not a family member).	30	
Change in number of arguments with spouse or partner.	30	
Mortgage or loan for a major purpose.	25	
Foreclosure of mortgage or loan.	25	
Sleep less than eight hours per night.	25	
Change in responsibilities at work.	25	
Trouble with in-laws, or with children.	25	
Outstanding personal achievement.	25	
Spouse begins or stops work.	20	
Begin or end school.	20	
Change in living conditions (visitors in the home, change in roommates etc.).	20	
Change in personal habits (diet, exercise, smoking, etc.).	20	
Chronic allergies.	20	
Trouble with boss.	20	
Change in work hours or conditions.	15	
Moving to new residence.	15	
Presently in premenstrual period.	15	
Change in schools.	15	
Change in religious activities.	15	
Change in social activities (more or less than before).	15	
Minor financial loan.	10	
Change in frequency of family get-togethers.	10	
Have been, or are about to go, on holiday.	10	
Presently in Christmas season.	10	
Minor violation of the law.	5	
Total Score		

Table 4-1. Stress level of significant life events.

If this occurs you should:
- Ask for help, particularly when the task requirement is outside your expertise and/or capabilities;
- Communicate the ramifications of any unusual or unexpected results;
- Not deviate from procedures or take short cuts because of time pressure;
- Just do what you can. If you cannot do the job safely in the time available, complete the work that you can do, safely and professionally.

STRESS AND TIME PRESSURE IN SHIFT AND TASK HANDOVERS

Ironically, one of the busiest times in the maintenance environment is during shift and task handovers. Generally during this time, paperwork is being completed (in a rush) and a briefing prepared for the oncoming shift. Often, shifts and supervisors do not get the opportunity for a face to face handover.

The quality of information in shift and task handover notes varies from organization to organization, and sometimes is of a very poor standard. Where possible, it is best to have an overlap between shifts to ensure a face to face handover. In all cases, provide a written handover to the oncoming shift, team, or individual taking over a specific task. All organizations should have a formal process of providing clear information for task/shift handover to the incoming team.

Managing shift handovers?

Manage stress and time pressure during the shift handover by planning appropriately, and communicating. Before the shift ends, identify any obvious and appropriate points in the maintenance process needed to complete the work. The outgoing supervisor also needs to allow adequate time for all tasks (including completing any outstanding documentation) and for a comprehensive written shift handover log to be completed before the incoming shift's arrival. An example of a shift/task handover log is included in **Table 4-2**.

KEY POINTS
- High levels of stress are a problem for any individual or maintenance team The effects of stress are often subtle and difficult to assess.
- Stress is often described as being insidious; that is it develops slowly and has a gradual and cumulative effect. Stress can be well established before we are aware that it is degrading our performance.

SHIFT – TASK HANDOVER SHEET	
COMPANY	
SHIFT/TASK	
TIME/DATE	
Aircraft Registration	
Maintenance Procedure Reference	
Task Details	
Steps Completed	
Steps Required	
Power Restrictions	
Items/Equipment Disconnected for Access	
Test Equipment In Use	
Equipment/Tooling/GSE Deficiencies Identified	
Fault Finding Conducted	
Additional Information/Comments	
NAME	**TRADE/POSITION**

Table 4-2. Shift/task handover log.

- Inappropriately high levels of stress can degrade performance significantly, as a result, safety can also be compromised.
- Fitness for work is not just a physical condition, but also a psychological one. It involves being able to perceive, think, and act to the best of our ability without the hindering effects of stress, anger, worry and anxiety.
- Work overload occurs when the number and complexity of the tasks allocated to an individual or team exceed their ability to cope. As performance deteriorates, we are forced to shed tasks and focus on key information.
- If interrupted during a safety critical maintenance task, take appropriate steps to ensure there are no omitted or forgotten actions or procedural steps.
- To an individual, self imposed pressure is real and is no different from any actual pressure being applied to get the job done.
- Where possible, it is always best to have an overlap between shifts to ensure a face to face handover. In all cases however, a written handover should be provided to the oncoming shift or individual taking over a specific task.
- Before the shift ends, identify an obvious and appropriate point in the maintenance process to complete the work, while also allowing sufficient time to complete the paperwork and brief the incoming supervisor.

WORKLOAD–OVERLOAD AND UNDERLOAD

Both arousal and alertness are necessary for us to achieve our optimum performance, however, too much, or too little arousal can adversely affect our ability to function effectively. It is therefore important for us to be aware of the symptoms of stress in ourselves and others as well as to understand the effect of stress on team performance as a whole.

The Yerkes Dodson (*Figure 4-1*) curve demonstrates that our performance is directly related to the level of arousal. The graph below shows that there is typically a level of arousal which aligns with the optimum level of performance. At very low levels of arousal (boredom) and very high levels of arousal (stress, anxiety and overload) our performance is very much degraded.

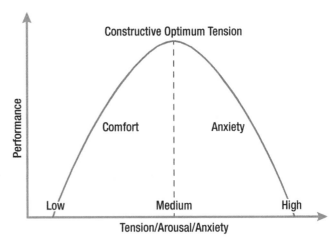

Figure 4-1. The Yerkes Dodson curve demonstrates how our level of arousal affects task performance.

FACTORS DETERMINING WORKLOAD

Maintenance tasks are process driven and usually follow a standard pattern and order, some of which we can control, and some we cannot. We have limited mental capacity to deal with information. We are also limited physically in terms of visual acuity, strength and dexterity. Therefore, workload must reflect the degree in which the demands of the task fall within our mental and physical capacities.

Workload is a relatively subjective measure (experienced differently by different people) and is affected by:
- The nature of the task, such as its physical and mental demands;
- The circumstances under which the task is performed: the standard of performance required, the time available to accomplish the task and the prevailing environmental factors;
- The individual and their situation: their skills both physical and mental; their experience, familiarity with the task; their health and fitness levels; and their emotional state.

WORK OVERLOAD

Work overload occurs when there is a lot of work to be done and the individual's or team's workload exceeds their ability to cope. As performance deteriorates, we are forced to shed tasks and focus on key information. In these situations error rates may also increase. As we carry out our assigned tasks, over a given time, the normal effects of fatigue will also produce a decline in our mental and physical capacity. (*Table 4-3*) This will mean that tasks that we consider easy at the beginning of our work period feel more difficult later on. Added to this, momentary workload spikes within a shift may strain our individual (or team) capacity, increasing the risk of errors.

Work overload can occur for a wide range of reasons, and may happen suddenly or gradually. It is good practice to plan maintenance tasks so that individuals (or the team as a whole) are not expected to perform at an unacceptable level to complete their tasks within the allocated time. Specific task allocation between team members can reduce the likelihood of one person within the team being overloaded.

Maintenance personnel under excessive workload (often associated with unrealistic time pressures) can exhibit or experience the following issues.

HIGH WORKLOAD	
Omission and Filtering	Ignoring some signals or responsibilities that are not seen as immediately relevant or necessary.
Reduced ability to think logically:	Limited capability for the consideration of other possibilities, or to process information correctly.
Queuing	Delaying required actions/responses in the hope that you will be able to catch up as the task progresses.
Confirmation Bias	The tendency to automatically confirm a decision we have made, ignoring other information to the contrary.
Approximation	Near enough becomes good enough.
Regression	Reverting to a previously well learned procedure or action which may or may not be appropriate for the current task.

Table 4-3. Typical sound levels for various activities.

Causes of High Workload

Typically, high workload within the aviation maintenance environment flows from the following issues:

• Poor task planning;
• Unexpected events;
• Inadequate manning/high tempo;
• Changing task requirements;
• System design/access problems;
• System/task complexity

The following case study demonstrates how inadequate staffing can lead to poor maintenance practices:

CASE STUDY: SHORT HANDED!

Shoddy maintenance by an overworked mechanical staff has been cited as a significant contributing factor in the crash of a helicopter in Ponte Vedra Beach, Florida on 27 March 2007 that fatally injured two people, according to the National Transportation Safety Board (NTSB). A mechanic told the NTSB that the crew was understaffed and forgot to check parts.

The pilot instructor and student passenger were killed when the single engine Robinson R44 helicopter crashed minutes after leaving the airport. An initial crash report said key bolts, nuts and washers were missing from the flight control system.

The NTSB report said a mechanic with the company that owned the helicopter told investigators that missing and loosened hardware that caused the chopper to crash near the ocean was the result of understaffing and staffers being 'pulled in all directions by company personnel'. In response to the accident, the operator has changed policies and procedures to ensure more mechanics per shift, more thorough inspections and fewer interruptions for mechanics.

The mechanic who worked on the helicopter told NTSB investigators that the operator had too few maintenance personnel and that, a few nights before the crash, an apprentice wanted to stay late with the mechanic and finish a section of the inspection. 'As a result, the mechanic forgot to go back and secure the hardware,' the report says. A 30 minute test flight didn't reveal the problem.

AIRCRAFT
TECHNICAL
BOOK COMPANY

The operator's lead mechanic told investigators that staff were being pushed to get the helicopter ready to fly while also being involved in working on several other aircraft, shopping for tools, and preparing an estimate for a crash repair in Melbourne.

WORK UNDERLOAD

Although rare in the maintenance environment, work under load does occur. Work under load can result from menial, simple or very repetitive tasks that are boring, or indeed from a lack of tasks to do. We are likely to be less attentive when carrying out repetitive tasks; boredom may set in and may begin to raise the level of mental stimulation by thinking about things not related to the task, (e.g. what to do at the weekend). Under these conditions, situational awareness is degraded and errors and omissions will increase.

SLEEP AND FATIGUE, SHIFT WORK

FATIGUE

We use the word fatigue all the time, but what exactly does it mean? There are several different meanings of the word:
- Tiredness after hard physical work;
- Emotional fatigue;
- Short term effects of intense concentration on a task;
- An overwhelming need to sleep.

Fatigue can have a major effect on your safety and the quality of your work when you are maintaining aircraft. We can distinguish between two types of sleep related fatigue:
- Acute—this is generally only short term and can be remedied with a good night's sleep
- Chronic—a longer term problem, as there is usually a buildup of sleep deprivation.

Fatigue can act like a toxin accumulating in our body. We can generally deal with a small amount of it, and work it out of our system by catching up on a night's sleep, but chronic fatigue accumulates and can have increasingly dangerous effects.

The Effects of Fatigue

One obvious hazard of fatigue is that the fatigued person loses the fight to stay awake while at work. Clearly this is most dangerous when the person is operating equipment or driving a vehicle.

A sleep episode can take the form of a micro sleep, which is a brief moment (generally between 2-30 seconds) when the person starts to enter the first stage of sleep, possibly with their eyes still open; sometimes for less than a few seconds before regaining consciousness. The person is typically unaware that they have experienced a micro sleep, and may continue to perform simple repetitive tasks while asleep. When truck drivers volunteered to wear sleep monitoring equipment while they worked, researchers were amazed to find that some drivers were showing signs of the first stage of sleep while driving on interstate highways.

Sleep deprivation can produce effects very similar to those produced by alcohol. An Australian study found that people who were given a simple task in the early hours of the morning, after being awake for 17 hours, performed as badly as if they had a blood alcohol concentration of .05 percent. Seven or more hours of wakefulness can produce impairment similar to that produced by a blood alcohol concentration of 0.10 percent. In other words, conducting a complex task when you are fatigued is like drinking on the job.

Consider These Two Imaginary Scenarios

Scenario 1

You are about to take your first parachute jump. You are handed your newly packed parachute by your instructor, Bob. He proudly tells you that he has just prepared your chute for you. You notice that Bob is leaning a little unsteadily on the rigging table. You also smell alcohol on his breath. When you ask Bob about this, he shrugs and tells you that he always likes to have a few shots of vodka to steady his hand before he starts rigging chutes.

Scenario 2

You are about to board a Cessna 172 for a brief flight. The aircraft has just come out of major maintenance. You speak with your colleague, Jim, who is also an AMT. He is normally a cheerful and talkative person, but on this day he has bags under his eyes and does not have much to say, except that he is looking forward to going home and having a good sleep. He tells you he has just worked 24 hours straight and is exhausted. He says his last job was a routine task, but for some reason he had trouble focusing on it. This last job involved replacing the aileron control cables on the aircraft you are about to board.

Is there a difference between these two scenarios? The above scenarios suggest that the performance of both Bob and Jim is impaired, the difference being what has caused that impairment—alcohol or fatigue. Just like someone who is intoxicated, if you are fatigued you will react more slowly, have trouble paying attention, be prone to memory lapses, and can show impaired judgment. You may also become withdrawn and uncommunicative. Boring tasks requiring close attention (such as some inspection jobs) are most affected by fatigue. Just as a drunk person may think they are sober, fatigued people often don't realize just how impaired they are.

Society doesn't tolerate drunk drivers or intoxicated workers. There is increasing awareness that the impairment resulting from severe fatigue is also no longer acceptable in safety critical environments such as aircraft hangars. Therefore, there should be no difference in the way we view and take action on the behavior of Bob and Jim described above—both are unsafe. The effects of fatigue on performance are summarized in ***Table 4-4.***

EFFECTS OF FATIGUE	
PERFORMANCE CATEGORY	**EFFECTS**
Attention: Reduced	Leave out steps in tasks.
	Preoccupation with single tasks or steps.
	Tunnel vision, less likely to notice the unexpected.
	Less aware or poor performance.
	Concentration requires more effort.
Memory: Diminished	Poor memory for tasks completed or underway.
	Forget to perform task steps.
	Revert to 'old habits'.
	More likely to forget to return to interrupted tasks.
Mood: Withdrawn	Reduced communication.
	More irritable, frustrated by minor difficulties.
	Temptation to shortcut tasks.
Reaction Time: Increased	Slower to notice problems.
	Less smooth control of equipment or vehicles.

Table 4-4. Effects of fatigue on performance.

Fatigue can affect all maintenance tasks, whether it is because of impaired judgment, difficulty in focusing attention, or other performance deficiencies. Two common types of fatigue related errors in maintenance:

Memory Failures

Fatigued AMTs are more likely to forget to perform routine actions, such as replacing oil caps and are more susceptible to distraction and resulting memory lapses.

Failures to Notice Defects or Problems

Fatigued AMTs have more difficulty detecting defects during inspections, and may be less likely to notice problems as a result of inattention or poor concentration. The reduced performance caused by fatigue imposes a burden on the aviation industry not only in terms of flight safety, but also in financial costs through delays, the need for rework, and other inefficiencies.

For example, a turn back of an airliner caused by a relatively simple error such as a gear lock pin left in place, can cost tens of thousands of dollars.

As the upper mount bolts were being torqued, the torque wrench being used broke. Another torque wrench was obtained, but it was noticed that it was out of calibration. The AMT performing the work and I discussed this and rationalized that "it was only out of calibration by a month or two". We decided to continue the procedure using the out of calibration wrench. When it was brought to my attention the following night, I immediately arranged to have the aircraft grounded and a torque check done. I don't want to sound like I was making excuses, but I believe this occurrence is a result of fatigue and stress. During the previous seven days, both myself and the other AMT had worked long hours. Over the previous 30 days I had three days off. In hindsight, I should have recognized then that I was badly in need of some rest. Instead, I pressed on.

Are we the best judges of our level of fatigue?

People are notoriously bad judges of their own level of fatigue. Asking a fatigued person if they are OK to keep working is like asking someone who is drunk if they are OK to drive. Even if we are not good judges of how tired we are, we can still keep track of how long we have been awake, how much sleep we have had recently, and the quality of that sleep. Before starting work, you could ask yourself these couple of questions.

- How much sleep have I been getting over the last few nights?
- How long have I been awake?
- Will I be working at a time when I would rather be sleeping?
- Have I had good quality sleep?

Your answers to these questions can help you assess how likely you are to be at risk because of fatigue.

The Impact of Fatigue in the Workplace

Some people in the aviation industry see fatigue as a normal and unavoidable part of aviation maintenance. They consider that with enough effort, a tired worker can continue to perform their job effectively. Increased effort or concentration might help for a few minutes, but it cannot compensate for fatigue over an entire shift. Fatigue has a very real detrimental impact on safety in aviation and in many other industries. *Table 4-5* shows some myths about sleep and fatigue.

Human error is recognized as a causal factor in the majority of industrial and transport accidents. Fatigue, in turn, is one of the major causes of human error. Here are some facts about the role of fatigue in industrial and transport accidents:

- Industrial and engineering disasters, including those involving nuclear power, tend to occur in disproportionate numbers in the early hours of the morning.
- Shift workers have twice the number of highway accidents as workers on day schedules.
- Fatigue is involved in 31 per cent of truck accidents resulting in the death of the driver
- Driving while sleepy is as dangerous as driving while intoxicated. In some parts of the world, a driver can be charged with motor vehicle homicide if they cause a fatality and have not slept in 24 hours. In Australia, road safety legislation now views motor vehicle accidents involving fatigue as 'voluntary impairment'–in other words you make a conscious choice to drive when tired.
- Fatigue is the largest identifiable and preventable cause of incidents in Australian transport operations. 20-30% of road accidents involve driver fatigue; 5-15% for fatal road accidents
- Australian road statistics show that sleep deprived individuals are 4–7 times more likely to have an incident driving to and from work.

MYTH	REALITY
Five or six hours of sleep a night is generally enough.	Very few people can manage on this amount of sleep without being seriously affected.
Daytime sleep is just as good as nighttime sleep.	Shift workers who have to sleep during the day generally get lower quality sleep and less of it.
We can judge how fatigued we are accurately.	Studies have shown that fatigued people often don't realize that their abilities are impaired by fatigue.
We need less sleep as we get older.	We still need the same amount of sleep, but our sleep becomes more fragmented, and we tend to wake earlier.

Table 4-5. Sleep and fatigue myths.

Fatigue is caused by a combination of two processes; sleep debt and circadian rhythms.

Sleep Debt

Adults generally sleep between seven and eight hours per night, although the need for sleep varies with some individuals needing up to 10 hours to remain alert. A century ago, before the widespread use of electric lighting, people typically slept around nine hours per night. Today, family demands, work commitments, and even television habits combine to limit the opportunities for nighttime sleep. In our busy world, many people are suffering from sleep deprivation without being aware of it. Extreme sleep deprivation has severe health effects, but even mild sleep deprivation can affect health and our ability to perform tasks in our work and personal lives.

If we obtain less sleep than we need, we build up a sleep debt. Each successive night of inadequate sleep adds to the debt. Even reducing our sleep by just one hour each night over several nights (getting seven hours when we really need eight) can reduce our mental efficiency. Shift workers, who sleep during daylight hours, also build up a sleep debt because daytime sleep tends to be briefer and of poorer quality than sleep obtained at night.

Obviously, a sleep debt may build up when a person's work and family commitments do not allow them to sleep for as long as their body needs. But sleep debts can also occur when sleep is disrupted by alcohol, drugs, and medical conditions. Medical conditions that can cause sleep disruption include the following:

- **Insomnia** – An inability to get to sleep, or a difficulty staying asleep. In many cases, insomnia is a symptom of another problem, such as medical conditions, side effects of medicines, or sleep disorders. Insomnia can also be caused by worry or emotional upsets.

- **Restless legs syndrome (RLS)** – A disorder that causes a strong urge to move your legs. This urge to move often occurs with strange and unpleasant feelings such as creeping, tingling, or burning. Moving your legs relieves the urge and the unpleasant feelings.
- **Periodic limb movements (PLM)** – Involuntary leg movements while asleep. The movements often disrupt sleep and may cause the person to wake up.
- **Sleep apnea** – A disorder in which breathing pauses or becomes shallow during sleep (see next page).

If you think you may be experiencing any of these conditions, see your doctor immediately.

Sleep Apnea

Sleep apnea is one of the more common medical conditions related to sleep disturbance. It is a condition in which breathing stops for ten seconds or longer during sleep. This reduces the level of oxygen to the brain and results in disturbed sleep. The condition is often associated with snoring. During a typical episode of sleep apnea snoring stops as the person ceases breathing. After a period of silence, they wake up, gasp or snort, and then return to snoring.

Sleep apnea affects between two and five per cent of the population. However, the condition is more common in men who are overweight and/or have a large neck size. Sleep apnea typically results in excessive daytime sleepiness. It also causes forgetfulness, clumsiness on tasks requiring careful movements, and may lead to reduced sex drive and/or impotence. The good news is that effective treatments are available for sleep apnea. As well as weight loss, your doctor may recommend surgery, or the use of a device that will keep your airway open while you sleep.

AIRCRAFT TECHNICAL BOOK COMPANY

When to see a doctor?

Consult a medical professional if you experience, or if your partner observes the following:
- Snoring loudly enough to disturb the sleep of others or yourself
- Shortness of breath that awakens you from sleep
- Intermittent pauses in your breathing during sleep
- Excessive daytime drowsiness, which may cause you to fall asleep while you're working, watching television, or even driving.

Circadian Rhythms

Our bodies have very steady 24 hour rhythms in their physiology, biochemistry and behavior. Alertness, body temperature, sleep tendency, and human error have also been shown to follow a 24 hour pattern. This is known as circadian rhythms. (*Figure 4-2*)

Our body's internal clock is kept on correct time by exposure to light, particularly early morning light. Our circadian rhythms are so reliable that even if we are removed from the 24 hour rhythm of night and day (such as wintering in Antarctica) the rhythms continue to run. Without regular exposure to a daily cycle of light and dark, circadian rhythms eventually begin to 'free run' and will no longer align closely with the 24 hour day.

Circadian rhythms have an important role in regulating sleep patterns. Chemical changes occur in the body as it prepares for sleep, typically between 8pm and midnight. Body temperature reaches a low point at around 3am, and then begins rising steadily as our body gets ready for the day ahead, even before we are naturally awake.

Do shift workers adapt to permanent night shifts?

Not usually! Research shows that fewer than 30% of permanent night shift workers actually adjust their rhythms to a nighttime schedule. In most cases, they remain on a typical daytime pattern. As a result, even workers on regular night shifts will still experience a strong drive for sleep during the night, and will find it more difficult to obtain good quality rest during daylight hours.

Beware the WOCL!

The period from around 2am–5am when we would normally be asleep is often referred to as the Window of Circadian Low (WOCL), and is a time when mental functioning is generally at its worst. The WOCL is a high risk time for human error. Even people without a sleep debt find that their work performance is affected by fatigue during the WOCL, but a sleep debt will intensify the negative effects of the WOCL.

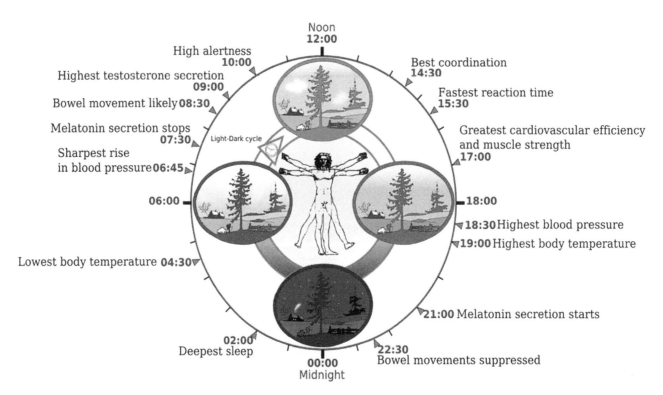

Figure 4-2. Circadian rhythms.

Studies of thousands of industrial errors have shown that although they can occur at any time of day or night, a large proportion of errors occur at around 3am. There is often a second, although smaller risk period at around 3pm. That afternoon period is sometimes called the 'post lunch dip', but it happens regardless of whether people eat lunch or not.

In a recent study, hundreds of errors reported by AMTs anonymously were examined to see how they varied throughout the 24 hour day. (*Figure 4-3*) Nearly all the errors were minor and were quickly corrected. Most of these several hundred errors were absent minded ones made during routine or monotonous tasks such as refitting caps and covers, removing tools, and positioning stands and equipment. Problem solving mistakes such as misdiagnosed faults were less common.

The results showed that absent minded errors showed a strong circadian rhythm, with a big peak between 2am and 3am. Problem solving mistakes, on the other hand, happened at all times of the day and night. Although the cases came from airlines, the same pattern was observed in general aviation, even though overnight work is generally less common.

These results remind us to be alert to the dangers of fatigue. Everyone involved in maintenance, needs to be aware that it is harder to focus your attention during the Window of Circadian Low (WOCL). This in turn may increase the odds of errors, particularly absentminded slips and memory lapses.

Tips for dealing with the WOCL: 2–5am
- If possible, avoid the most safety critical tasks during the WOCL. For example, if you have a choice of rigging flight controls or checking the expiration dates on life jackets, leave the flight controls until later;
- If you can, keep the lights bright and the temperature slightly cool;
- Try to avoid monotonous or tedious tasks;
- Ask someone to check your work;
- Stretch, walk around. Get some fresh air. But don't expect this to help for more than a few minutes;
- If you can, take a brief nap. Even a few minutes will help;
- Use caffeine carefully, and be aware that it may make it more difficult to sleep when you get home.

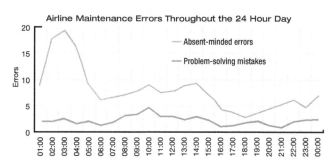

Figure 4-3. Airline maintenance errors throughout the 24 hour day.

Factors that increase the impact of fatigue.
Certain conditions in the workplace can make the effects of fatigue more severe. These include:
- Low light: A work environment with low illumination reduces alertness and makes it harder for a fatigued person to fight the urge to sleep.
- Passive activities: Tasks which are boring, do not involve physical activity, or are performed while seated, are more likely to be affected by fatigue. Tasks requiring continuous monitoring or long tedious inspections tend to be more susceptible to fatigue related errors.
- Warm temperature: A fatigued person will find it harder to stay alert if their work environment is warm.

Case Study

Two of us worked together that night on the fan lube. My partner cleaned and resprayed the dampers. Unknown to him, one damper fell off the shelf where he was working and landed, out of sight. Upon reassembly, I sat in the inlet installing blades and dampers. Apparently I missed installing a damper under #20 fan blade. This occurs occasionally, and you'll have an extra damper left over after all the fan blades are installed. Then you spin the fan slowly and find where the missing damper is. But in this case, we had no 'extra' damper because, unknown to us, it had fallen to a lower shelf on the work table. Inspection looked over the blade installation (they don't look at dampers) and gave us an OK to install front spinners. The aircraft left the station on a flight the next morning and upon reaching its destination, the pilot wrote up a vibration on #2 engine.

"I think the major factor in this instance was alertness. The human body is not designed to work the night shift. I cannot function at my best during the night. I routinely get four hours of restless sleep a day, and I'm constantly tired and irritable."

Managing the risks of fatigue in aviation maintenance.
Over 40 per cent of adults in the general population report that daytime sleepiness is affecting the quality of their work. AMTs tend to be even more fatigued than the general population. In fact, 82 per cent of maintenance personnel worldwide consider that fatigue is a safety issue in aircraft maintenance. In 2001, a study using sleep monitoring equipment showed that maintenance personnel:

- Sleep an average of only five hours per 24 hour period;
- Tend to over estimate the amount of sleep they are getting;
- Work an average of 48 hours per week;
- 10% say they have fallen asleep at the wheel while commuting.

Sleep Inertia (aka 'Sleep Drunkenness')

In the few minutes after waking up, we may experience a brief period of confusion, poor memory and grogginess. This effect, which can last up to 15 minutes, is known as sleep inertia. It can be an issue in workplaces where people have to wake up shortly before they get to work, for example pilots who sleep in onboard crew rest facilities. It can also be an issue in maintenance if you are on call during the night. Be aware that after waking from a deep sleep it might take 15 minutes or so before you are alert enough to get to work.

Fatigue cannot be eliminated, but the risks associated with it can be managed through a partnership between employer and employee. Some of the causes of fatigue originate with company policies; for example, hours of work, the extent to which work is performed during the night, and the predictability of work schedules. Other causes stem from the employee's personal situation, including commuting time, family responsibilities, and the demands of second jobs.

Figure 4-4 shows some of the main sources of fatigue. Employer and employee each share responsibility for managing fatigue.

How tired are you?

Epworth sleepiness scale

Developed by Dr Murray Johns of Epworth Hospital in Melbourne

How likely are you to doze off or fall asleep in the following situations, in contrast to just feeling tired? This refers to your usual way of life over recent times. Even if you have not done some of these things recently, try to work out how they would have affected you. Use the following scale to choose the most appropriate number for each situation:

no chance of dozing	slight chance of dozing	moderate chance of dozing	high chance of dozing
0	1	2	3

Situation	Chance of dozing
Sitting and reading	
Watching TV	
Sitting inactive in a public place (e.g. a theatre or a meeting)	
As a passenger in a car for an hour without a break	
Lying down to rest in the afternoon when circumstances permit	
Sitting and talking to someone	
Sitting quietly after a lunch without alcohol	
In a car, while stopped for a few minutes in traffic	

1 – 6. Congratulations, you are getting enough sleep!
7 – 8. Your score is average
9 and up. Seek the advice of a sleep specialist without delay!

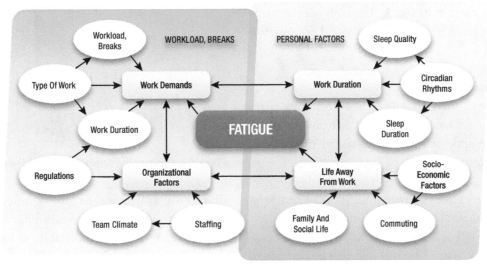

Figure 4-4. Employer and employee responsibilities for managing stress.

Responsibilities of the Employer:
- Schedule work hours and time off to give the employee sufficient opportunity for restorative sleep.
- Manage workload and breaks.

Responsibilities of the Employee:
- Manage personal time to make sure you are rested and fit for duty.
- When reporting incidents, note if fatigue was a factor.

Strategies to Deal with Fatigue

Some of these might be considered common sense, but others may not be as obvious.

Get More Sleep!
The first and most obvious way to prevent fatigue is to get more good quality sleep. This is easier said than done, particularly if you work irregular hours, have a second job, or have young children.

Controlled Naps
Numerous research studies have shown that even a brief nap can result in performance improvements. Napping used to be widely discouraged by employers, but now pilots, air traffic controllers and others are being allowed to take brief controlled naps when workload permits.

Here are two types of naps:

Preventative Nap
- A brief sleep before you report for work, particularly before starting a night shift.

Restorative Nap
- A brief sleep during a break at work can sharpen your performance for the next couple of hours.

There are two problems to watch out for with naps:
- Avoid taking naps in the hours before you go to bed so as not to interfere with your main sleep period.
- Naps lasting more than about 40 minutes may produce sleep inertia, (a feeling of grogginess that may persist after awakening). The best nap duration appears to be about 20-25 minutes.

Caffeine

Caffeine is one of the most widely used stimulants, and if used carefully and in moderation can be part of an overall fatigue management strategy. Caffeine has a half life in the body of around five hours, so shift workers should be careful to avoid caffeine in the hours leading up to sleep. If you use caffeine to stay alert at work, use it selectively, and cut down on caffeinated drinks at other times. If you develop a tolerance to caffeine, it will not be as effective in keeping you alert.

Breaks
If the situation allows, a brief break or a stretch can help to focus your attention and provide temporary relief from fatigue. Do not be afraid to call time out for a

few minutes to clear your head. Breaks however, only provide a short term benefit. The only real remedy for fatigue is sleep.

Progressive Restrictions

One way to deal with fatigue in maintenance is to keep those who are most fatigued away from the most critical tasks, an approach sometimes called 'progressive restrictions'. (**Figure 4-5**)

Some companies have internal policies progressively limiting the tasks an AMT can perform the longer they have been at work. For example, an AMT who has been on duty for longer than 12 hours might not be permitted to certify the work of others, or may not be permitted to perform engine runs or other critical tasks.

Key Points

- Fatigue seriously impairs work performance and increases the chances of human error.
- With no legally imposed duty time limits, maintenance personnel are often pressured to work extremely long hours, and almost certainly experience greater levels of fatigue than most other sectors of the aviation industry.
- In the past there was a common attitude that people should just tough it out, but it is now increasingly recognized that fatigue can produce performance impairments comparable to alcohol. Drunk driving is no longer tolerated by society, and there are signs that social attitudes are also shifting when it comes to fatigue. In the near future, performing a safety critical task while fatigued may be seen as reckless an act as drunk driving.
- There is a worldwide move towards comprehensive fatigue risk management systems (FRMS) in maintenance operations. These systems typically include awareness training, incident reporting systems, risk assessment and controls to limit the impact of fatigue. Even without a full FRMS, maintenance organizations can still take steps to manage fatigue through simple steps such as on duty time limits.

SHIFT WORK

Most aircraft movements occur between 6am and 10pm to fit in with the requirements of passengers. AMTs are required when aircraft are on the ground such as during turn arounds. However, this scheduling means that

Figure 4-5. Employer and employee responsibilities for managing stress.

aircraft are available for more significant maintenance over night. Thus, aircraft maintenance is clearly a 24 hour business and it is inevitable, to fulfill commercial obligations, that AMTs usually work shifts. Some permanently work the same shift, but the majority cycle through different shifts.

Advantages and Disadvantages of Shift Work

There are pros and cons to working shifts.

Advantages include:
- More days off
- Avoiding peak traffic times when traveling to work.

Disadvantages include:
- Working 'unsociable hours', meaning that time available with friends and family will be disrupted;
- Working when human performance is known to be poorer (i.e. between 4am and 6am);
- Problems associated with disturbance of the body's various rhythms (principally sleeping patterns).

Rolling Shift Patterns

When an AMT works rolling shifts and changes from one shift to another (e.g. 'day shift' to 'night shift'), the body's internal clock is not immediately reset. It continues on its old wake sleep cycle for several days. However, by this time, the AMT may have moved onto the next shift. Generally, it is now accepted that shift rotation should be to later shifts (Early Shift → Late Shift → Night Shift or Day Shift → Night Shift) instead of rotation towards earlier shifts. (**Figure 4-6**)

CONCLUSION

Most individuals need approximately 8 hours sleep in a 24 hour period, although this varies between individuals, some needing more and some happy with less to be fully refreshed. They can usually perform adequately with less than this for a few days, building up a temporary sleep

Figure 4-6. The proper shift rotation.

'deficit'. However, any sleep deficit will need to be made up, otherwise performance will start to suffer. A good rule of thumb is that one hour of high quality sleep is good for two hours of activity.

When rotating shifts are worked, it is important to be disciplined with eating and sleeping times. Moreover, after work activities have to be carefully planned. For example, it is obvious that an individual who has been out late night will not be adequately rested if on an early shift. Shift working patterns encountered may include three or four days off after the last night shift. It can be tempting to work additional hours or another job in one or more of these days off. This is especially the case when first starting a career and when financial pressures may be higher. Although most adapt to shift working, it becomes harder to work rotating shifts as one gets older.

ALCOHOL, MEDICATIONS, AND DRUG ABUSE

ALCOHOL

What is alcohol? The term alcohol describes a series of organic chemicals, but only one type, ethyl alcohol or ethanol, is found in drinks intended for human consumption. Alcohol is a central nervous system depressant as illustrated in *Figure 4-7* summarizing the various stages of intoxication.

How long does it take to eliminate alcohol from the body? *Figure 4-8* demonstrates how long it takes alcohol to be eliminated from the body, taking into account factors such as different rates for men and women, the number of drinks consumed, and the time over which drinking occurs. The calculations refer to standard size drinks. (*Figure 4-9*)

STAGES OF ALCOHOL INTOXICATION

BAC (g/100 ml of blood or g/210 l of breath)	Stage	Clinical symptoms
0.01 - 0.05	Subclinical	Behavior nearly normal by ordinary observation
0.03 - 0.12	Euphoria	• Mild euphoria, sociability, talkativeness • Increased self confidence; decreased inhibitions • Diminution of attention, judgment and control • Beginning of sensory motor impairment • Loss of efficiency in finer performance tests
0.09 - 0.25	Excitement	• Emotional instability; loss of critical judgment • Impairment of perception, memory and comprehension • Decreased sensory response; increased reaction time • Reduced visual acuity; peripheral vision and glare recovery • Lack of sensory motor coordination; impaired balance • Drowsiness
0.18 - 0.30	Confusion	• Disorientation, mental confusion; dizziness • Exaggerated emotional states • Disturbances of vision and of perception of colour, form, motion and dimensions • Increased pain threshold • Decreased muscular coordination; staggering gait; slurred speech • Apathy, lethargy
0.25 - 0.40	Stupor	• General inertia; approaching loss of motor functions • Markedly decreased response to stimuli • Marked decrease in muscular coordination; inability to stand or walk • Vomiting; incontinence • Impaired consciousness; sleep or stupor
0.35 - 0.50	Coma	• Complete unconsciousness • Depressed or abolished reflexes • Subnormal body temperature • Incontinence • Impairment of circulation and respiration • Possible death
0.45 +	Death	• Death from respiratory arrest

Figure 4-7. Stages of alcohol intoxication.

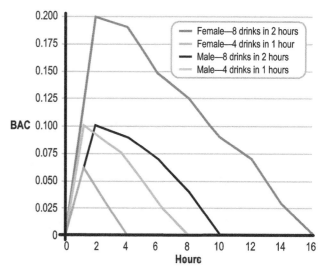

Figure 4-8. Hours required to return blood alcohol concentration (BAC) to zero.

Standard drink sizes are considered:
• 12-ounces of regular beer.
• 5-ounces of wine.
• 1.5-ounces of 80 proof distilled spirits.

Figure 4-9. The percent of "pure" alcohol, expressed here as alcohol by volume (alc/vol), varies by beverage.

Blood alcohol concentration depends on the amount of alcohol consumed and the rate at which the user's body metabolizes alcohol. The body metabolizes alcohol at a fairly constant rate. Ingesting alcohol at a rate higher than the rate of elimination results in a cumulative effect and an increasing blood alcohol concentration.

Alcohol and Safety

Alcohol is a depressant drug, even though it may feel stimulating at first. Within minutes of drinking, some alcohol will be absorbed into the bloodstream. Certain things, such as eating, affect the alcohol absorption rate; eating slows down absorption. Even a small amount of alcohol affects decision making skills. Your ability to perform certain tasks, such as trouble shooting is quickly affected.

Alcohol and Sleep

Alcohol has a detrimental effect on both the quality of sleep and on daytime attention. Sleep problems are common in alcoholics. The effects of alcohol on sleep and attention are complicated to define and have considerable variability in individuals.

Disturbance of Paradoxical (REM) Sleep/Slow Wave Sleep Cycle

Alcohol seems to accelerate falling asleep, at least in subjects who do not tend to fall asleep immediately. The negative effects arise later and affect the quality and duration of sleep. Sleep is a complex phenomenon. There are alternating phases of deep sleep, called paradoxical or REM sleep during which the subject dreams, and slow wave sleep. Undisturbed progression of these two phases of sleep is essential. Alcohol disturbs or interrupts this sequence. Thus alcoholics, and some people who have stopped drinking, complain about disturbed and fragmented sleep, frightening dreams, and insomnia.

The disruptive effects of alcohol last well into the night, even when alcohol has been eliminated. This is not a phenomenon specific to alcohol, and also seen with other sedative products. Snoring is abnormally frequent after drinking alcohol before going to bed. This is due to the relaxing effects of alcohol on the pharyngeal muscles.

Daytime Repercussions of Alcohol's Effects on Sleep

Disturbed sleep or sleep deprivation add to the sedative effects of alcohol during the day. Alcohol consumed late in the evening will noticeably reduce the performance of a subject (attention, dexterity) the following morning. By producing an accumulation of nights of poor sleep, alcohol can disrupt the normal sleep/wake cycle. Hence the negative effects of alcohol can have repercussions on daytime performance.

Alcohol and Attention

The sedative action of alcohol has variable effect on attention, reducing it and producing diminished performance. This action is particularly noticeable in subjects who lack sleep or who tend to be lethargic. Alcohol, even in moderate amounts, seems to reduce the ability of an individual to waken, to the point where driving ability is affected, not just in the hours after consumption, but sometimes for days afterwards.

What would you do?

One of your colleagues has arrived at work for an early shift, appears to be tired, has bloodshot eyes, and smells of alcohol. You have worked with this person a number of times before, and this behavior appears uncharacteristic. Your colleague acts as if things are normal and is preparing to start the shift. Do you:
• Turn a blind eye, ignore him, and hope for the best?

- Pull him aside and have a quiet chat, asking if anything is wrong? In your conversation, you suggest that if he has been drinking some time before work, he should call sick and go home.
- Go straight to your supervisor, saying you think your colleague may be under the influence and his ability could be impaired.
- Quietly suggest that he sees the supervisor himself, as you think he might be unfit for work. Remind him that being 'not fit for work', is unacceptable, given the potential safety implications.

Let's look at each of these options to see what might be the best and safest course of action.

Taking professionalism, personal standards, and most importantly safety into consideration, turning a blind eye is not advisable, and would even play on our own conscience. How would you feel if an incident involving your colleague, which you had the power to avoid occurred later?

Pulling him aside for a quiet chat may address the immediate problem on the day, but does nothing to address a potentially greater problem. Suggesting that he go home sick conveniently avoids the issue, but may mask problems with dependence.

Advising your supervisor passes on your responsibility to a higher authority and allows the issue to be dealt with according to organizational policies. However, the downside of this option is that you may be labeled a 'snitch', which this could create personal consequences for you and others in the future.

This then leaves you with the only choice–the last option. Should you suggest that he tell the supervisor himself? This is a difficult choice as it raises internal debates about what is right for them, right for us, right for the organization, as well as what is right and best in the interests of safety.

DRUGS

What is a drug? A drug is any substance (solid, liquid or gas) that brings about physical and/or psychological changes. The drugs of most concern in the community are those affecting the central nervous system. They act on the brain and can change the way you think, feel, or behave. These drugs are known as psychoactive drugs.

When we use drugs our capacity to think and move is generally impaired. The changes may be slight, but when involved in safety sensitive activities, drug use can lead to dangerous errors.

The effects of alcohol and other drugs include:
- Slowed processing of information;
- Slowed perception;
- Longer reaction time. Responses to hazards are slower, and the number of inappropriate avoidance maneuvers increases;
- Reduced coordination and ability to track or follow movement;
- Reduced ability to concentrate;
- Reduced ability to see alternative solutions, to think flexibly;
- Attention problems affecting:
  - Focused attention–concentrating on a single task;
  - Divided attention–coping with a number of sources of information at once;
  - Sustained attention–concentrating on one thing for some time;
  - Memory (including short term memory, and memory for visual and spatial information);
  - Increased risk taking.

How are drugs classified?
Drugs are commonly classified according to their legal status, and their effects on the central nervous system.

Legal Drugs
Laws control the availability, quality, and price of legal drugs. For example, in the United States, alcohol may not be sold to persons under the age of 21.

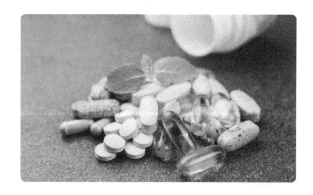

Illegal Drugs

Because they are illegal, there is no quality control on illicit drugs such as heroin and ecstasy. This means that users can never be sure that the drug they are taking is what they think it is.

For example, PMA (paramethoxyamphetamine), a toxic form of amphetamine, has been sold as ecstasy. The user also cannot be sure of a drug's strength or purity. Various batches of an illegally manufactured drugs may have different mixtures of the drug and additives such as talcum powder, caffeine, or even poisons.

Drugs Affecting the Central Nervous System

There are three main types of drug affecting the central nervous system: depressants, stimulants, and hallucinogens.

Depressants

Depressants slow down the functions of the central nervous system. Depressant drugs do not necessarily make a person feel depressed. In small quantities, depressants can cause the user to feel more relaxed and/or less inhibited. In large enough quantities they can cause unconsciousness, vomiting, and even death. Depressants affect concentration and coordination. They slow down the ability to respond to unexpected situations. Examples of depressants include:

- Alcohol;
- Cannabis;
- Barbiturates (Seconal, Tuinal and Amytal);
- Benzodiazepines (tranquilizers), such as Rohypnol, Valium, Serepax, Mogadon, Normison and Eupynos;
- GHB (gammahydroxybutrate), or Fantasy;
- Opiates and opioids, including heroin, morphine, codeine, and methadone;
- Some solvents and inhalants, many of which are common household products.

Stimulants

Stimulants on the other hand, act on the central nervous system to speed up the messages to and from the brain. They can make the user feel more awake, alert, or confident. Stimulants increase heart rate, body temperature, and blood pressure. Other effects include reduced appetite, dilated pupils, talkativeness, agitation, and sleep disturbance. Large quantities of stimulants can "over stimulate" the user, causing anxiety, panic, seizures, headaches, stomach cramps, aggression, and paranoia. Prolonged use of strong stimulants can mask some of the effects of depressant drugs, such as alcohol, making it difficult for a person to judge their effects.

- Mild stimulants include:
    - Ephedrine (used in medicines for bronchitis, hay fever, and asthma);
    - Caffeine (in coffee, tea, and cola drinks);
    - Nicotine (in tobacco).
- Stronger stimulants include:
    - Methamphetamines;
    - Cocaine;
    - MDMA/Ecstasy;
    - Slimming tablets (such as Duromine, Tenuate, Dospan and Ponderax).

Hallucinogens

Hallucinogens affect perception. People who have taken them may believe they see or hear things that aren't really there, or what they do see may be distorted in some way. The effects of hallucinogens vary a great deal, so it is impossible to predict how they will affect a particular person at a particular time.

Some effects of hallucinogens include dilation of pupils, loss of appetite, increased activity, talking or laughing, emotional euphoria and well being, jaw clenching, sweating, panic, paranoia, loss of contact with reality, irrational or bizarre behavior, stomach cramps, and nausea. Examples of hallucinogens include:

- Datura
- Ketamine
- LSD
- Magic mushrooms
- Cannabis is a hallucinogen and a depressant.
- Ecstasy can also have hallucinogenic qualities.

How do drugs affect people?

The effects of a drug depend on the type of drug, how much is used, how it is taken, the characteristics of the person taking it (body type and mood), and the situation or place at which the drug is taken.

Some factors to consider include:
- How much of the drug is taken and how often;
- How the drug is taken;
- A person's physical characteristics, such as height, weight, and gender;
- The person's mood and their environment;
- Tolerance to the drug;
- Other drugs used (poly/multiple drug use).

Legal Drugs – Prescription and Over the Counter
The following are some of the over the counter and prescription types of medication in common use and how they may affect you. This list is not exhaustive. You should take care to find out the likely effects of any prescribed drug before you take it. Always seek advice from your doctor and pharmacist, and in particular declare what kind of work you do so they can take that into account when prescribing medication.

Sleeping Tablets
These can dull the senses, cause mental confusion and slow reaction times. How long this effect lasts varies from person to person and may be unduly prolonged. You should seek expert medical advice before using them.

Antidepressants
These can depress the alerting system and have contributed to errors, in turn leading to fatal accidents. You should stop work when starting antidepressants and only return when it is clear that there are no adverse side effects. It is recommended that individuals seek medical advice from their appropriate medical specialist before returning to work.

Antibiotics
Penicillin and the various mycins and cyclines and sulphur drugs may have short term or delayed effects which can affect work performance. Their use indicates that a fairly severe infection may well be present and, apart from the effects of these substances themselves, the side effects of the infection will almost always render a person unfit for work.

Antihistamines
Such drugs are widely used in cold cures and in the treatment of hay fever, asthma, and allergic conditions. Many easily obtainable nasal spray and drops contain antihistamines. Most antihistamines tend to make the user feel drowsy, making operation of equipment or vehicles not recommended. Admittedly, very mild states of hay fever may be adequately controlled by small doses of anti allergic drugs, but a trial period to establish the absence of side effects is essential before going on duty. When individuals are affected by allergic conditions requiring more than the absolute minimum, and in all cases of asthma, you should seek medical advice.

'Pep' Pills: (containing caffeine, dexedrine, benzedrine)
Are used to maintain wakefulness can be habit forming. Individuals vary in their susceptibility to each drug, but all of them can create dangerous overconfidence. Over dosage may cause headaches, dizziness and mental disturbances. The use of 'pep' pills while working cannot be permitted. If tea or coffee is insufficient, you are not fit for work.

High Blood Pressure Medication
These are proving to be very effective in controlling this condition. However, antihypertensive agents all have some side effects, and should not be administered before adequate assessment of the need for treatment. Your doctor should be able to advise of any side effects you should consider.

Antimalarial Drugs
Antimalarial drugs prescribed in normally recommended doses do not usually have any adverse effects.

Oral Contraceptive Tablets
Oral contraceptive tablets in the standard dose do not usually have adverse effects, although regular supervision is required.

Sudafed
Sudafed is the trade name of a preparation containing pseudoephedrine hydrochloride. Your doctor may prescribe this for relief of nasal congestion. Side effects reported are anxiety, tremor, rapid pulse, and headache. The preparation does not contain antihistamines, which could sedate and cause drowsiness, but it can nevertheless affect skilled performance. Sudafed or similar medications, therefore, should not be taken when making maintenance decisions or performing safety critical tasks.

- The effects of Drugs and Alcohol are numerous. Even mild alcohol ingestion or impairment can degrade relevant skills and abilities, in turn increasing the risk of errors and subsequent incidents.
- A blood alcohol content of zero does not ensure safe operations. Post alcohol impairment must be acknowledged and managed as well.
- Maintenance personnel do safety critical work and should ensure that safety is put first. You have a duty to ensure that any medication you take will not put you or others at risk. There is no danger in seeking medical advice!

CONCLUSION

Our overall well being is crucial to the safety of aviation maintenance. Our physical health is effected by how we take care of our bodies including nutrition and exercise.

To maintain a safety culture in the workplace we need to be aware of how workload stresses such as time pressure, deadlines, and shift work influence our attention and performance. Likewise, outside influences such as domestic stress, sleep, alcohol, and drugs also can affect our performance. Being aware of how the above factors influence our abilities will help in maintaining a safe and error free environment.

Question: 4-1
What are the two kinds of stress that can influence performance?

Question: 4-5
Describe how sleep debt builds up.

Question: 4-2
What are some positive measures that AMTs can do to maintain fitness and health>

Question: 4-6
What is the Window of Circadian Low (WOCL); when is it most likely to occur?

Question: 4-3
What are some symptoms of stress that may influence an AMTs work?

Question: 4-7
What is sleep inertia and how long does it usually last?

Question: 4-4
What are the effects of alcohol and drugs that may be evident?

Question: 4-8
What is the definition of a drug?

ANSWERS

Answer: 4-1

Work related stress (which can be real or imagined);
Domestic stress that results from life changes such as
divorce, birth of a child, or death of someone close,
moving, etc.

Answer: 4-2

Eating regular meals and a well balanced diet;
Regular exercise;
Stop smoking;
Sensible alcohol intake.

Answer: 4-3

Physiological symptoms–sweating, dryness of mouth;
Heath effects such as nausea, headaches,
sleep problems;
Behavioral symptoms, such as shaking, changes to
appetite, excessive drinking;
Cognitive effects such as poor communication;
Subjective effects such as anxiety, depression, aggression.

Answer: 4-4

Slowed processing;
Longer reaction time;
Reduced coordination;
Reduced ability to concentrate;
Reduced ability to see alternative solutions;
Attention problems.

Answer: 4-5

When we obtain less sleep then we need, we build up
sleep debt. Each successive night of inadequate sleep
adds to the deficit.

Answer: 4-6

The Window of Circadian Low is when mental
function is at its worst. It is most likely to occur
between the hours of 2am–5am.

Answer: 4-7

When we wake up we usually experience a brief period
of confusion, poor memory and grogginess. This can
last up to 15 minutes.

Answer: 4-8

A drug is any substance (solid/liquid/gas) that brings
about physical and/or psychological changes.

HUMAN FACTORS

PHYSICAL ENVIRONMENT

SUB-MODULE 05

	B1	B2

Sub-Module 05

PHYSICAL ENVIRONMENT

Knowledge Requirements

9.5 - Physical Environment

    Noise and fumes;

    Illumination;

    Climate and temperature;

    Motion and vibration;

    Working environment.

B1	B2
1	1

PHYSICAL ENVIRONMENT

9.5- PHYSICAL ENVIRONMENT

INTRODUCTION
This chapter considers the impact of noise, fumes, illumination, climate and temperature, motion and vibration, confined spaces and other issues that can adversely affect safety, productivity, and the health of personnel.

NOISE AND FUMES

NOISE
Noise in the workplace can have both short term and long term negative effects: it can be annoying, can interfere with verbal communication and mask warnings, and can damage workers' hearing (either temporarily or permanently). The ear is sensitive to sounds between certain frequencies (20 HZ to 20 KHz). The intensity of sound is measured in decibels (dB), where exposure in excess of 115 dB without ear protection even for a short duration is not recommended. This equates to standing within several hundred feet of a moving jet aircraft.

Noise is any unwanted sound, especially if it is loud, unpleasant and annoying. General background noise can be 'filtered out' by the brain through focused attention. For more problematic noise, some form of hearing protection (e.g. ear plugs and ear muffs), (*Figure 5-1*) is commonly used by technicians, both on the line and in the hangar to help with concentration. The noise environment can vary considerably. For instance, the airport ramp or apron area is clearly noisy, due to running aircraft engines or auxiliary power units (APUs), moving vehicles and so on. It is not unusual for this to exceed 85 dB–90 dB which can cause hearing damage if the time of exposure is prolonged. The hangar area can also be noisy, usually due to the use of various tools during aircraft maintenance. Short periods of intense noise are not uncommon and can cause temporary hearing loss. AMTs move to and from these noisy areas into the relative quiet of rest rooms, aircraft cabins, stores and offices.

It is very important that on duty Aircraft Maintenance Technicians (AMTs) remain aware of the extent of the noise. Some form of hearing protection should be carried at all times and used when remaining in an area where normal speech cannot be heard clearly at 2 yards. AMTs often need to discuss matters relating to a task with colleagues and also, at the end of a shift, handover to an incoming AMT. It is important that noise does not impair the ability to communicate, as this could be a safety issue. Important matters are discussed away from noisy areas.

Protecting Your Hearing

Know Your Work Environment
Building and maintaining aircraft requires a variety of power tools which use air compressors and generators. Ground equipment associated with moving aircraft also generates noise. Understanding the source of noise in your environment is the first step in preventing hearing loss. Consumer electronics stores sell inexpensive sound level meters for fine tuning the audio response on stereo systems. The same meter captures a wide decibel range, so it can be used in the hangar to monitor noisy operations.

Select Appropriate Hearing Protection Devices
Hearing Protection Devices (HPD) include earmuffs that cover the ear, ear plugs that insert into the ear canal and canal caps which cover the entrance to the ear canal. Which one should you use? Canal caps are for intermittent noise exposure such as ground crewmen or supervisors whose noise exposure is limited to brief trips to the ramp. Earmuffs and ear plugs are the more appropriate HPD for professional mechanics and anyone spending time in hangars. In the market place the foam earplug is the most common. *Figure 5-1* depicts approved HPD devices.

Figure 5-1. Two varieties of hearing protection from simple foam plugs to full earmuff; each offering protection (noise reduction) from 25–30 dB.

FUMES, CHEMICALS, TOXIC METALS AND SOLVENTS

The maintenance of aircraft involves working with a variety of hydraulic fluids, paints, cleaning compounds, and solvents. AMTs will also be exposed to aircraft fuel and exhaust. In fact, there is every possibility that an AMT could be exposed to a number of solvents and chemicals during their daily work. The following is a list of some chemicals AMTs are exposed to, and some recommended safety actions.

Chemicals

Gasoline Engine Exhaust (Carbon Monoxide)

Carbon Monoxide (CO) is both odorless and colorless. Symptoms of CO exposure are not immediately apparent, but no matter how small, any amount of exposure severely affects the function of sensitive tissues like the brain. Moderate CO poisoning results in headache, rapid breathing, nausea, weakness, confusion, and discoloration of the lips and nail beds. High exposures result in the loss of consciousness without other symptoms. Headache, nausea and vomiting start with lower exposures, while confusion and collapse, followed by death may occur with high exposure.

Survivors of CO poisoning often show delayed effects that appear two to forty days after an apparent complete recovery. The most frequently reported symptoms are mental deterioration including apathy, disorientation, amnesia, and irritability. Other symptoms include mood disorders, unusual behaviors, irrational speech content, and gait movement disorders.

AMTs are likely to encounter CO in ground equipment, such as fueling trucks and tugs. Unlike most automobiles, exhaust from ground support trucks is usually routed to the front instead of the rear of the vehicle. Refueling trucks spend a lot of time with their engines idling, allowing more CO to enter the cab. Small engines can produce CO that is just as deadly as that produced by these larger engines.

Here is a list of some safety strategies to minimize the risks to AMTs:
- Do not allow the use or operation of gasoline powered engines or tools inside hangars, even if the doors are open, unless the engine can be located outside and away from air intakes;

- Keep engines tuned, minimizing the production of CO;
- Recognize the symptoms of CO overexposure: headache, nausea, weakness, dizziness, visual disturbance, personality changes and loss of consciousness;
- When possible, use compressed air tools or tools powered by electricity rather than those powered by a gasoline engine;
- Place a CO monitor in the work area, truck cab, cockpit, or on yourself.

A coworker exhibiting any of the mentioned signs of over exposure demands the same treatment as if the individual were found unconscious. The following actions are recommended prior to emergency room admission:
- Remove victim from the work area into fresh air;
- Note any abrasions or other evidence of trauma that may have occurred if the victim fell while unconscious;
- Administer 100% breathing oxygen if available;
- Keep victim warm and protected and prepare for transport to an emergency room.

Kerosene Based Fuels

Kerosene based fuels include both jet and diesel fuels. Respiratory exposures to jet fuel are low for most AMTs, but symptoms include:
- Transient memory deficit (difficulty recalling even common items such as your phone number)
- Disturbances in consciousness (slow thinking, sense of drunkeness, light headed, slurring words)
- Irritation to eyes and nose (sneezing, runny nose)
- Nausea and vomiting
- Headache
- Staggering

Symptoms can persist for a time, but no published reports describe human deaths associated with a single jet fuel exposure. Skin absorption symptoms include:
- *Erythema* – reddening of the skin.
- *Eczema* – scaling and flaking of the skin.
- *Dermatitis* – thinning of the skin with redness and inflammation.

Other than entry into the fuel cell, exposure to fuel vapor is not sufficient enough to warrant use of a respirator. Fuel is a hydrocarbon that is easily removed

with good quality soap. Do not use other solvents to remove fuel from the skin. Common sense strategies to reduce exposure to fuels are:

- *Skin*
    - Use impervious gloves.
    - Wipe hands clean of fuel.
    - Wash with a good quality non abrasive soap.
    - Do not wash your skin with another solvent.
- *Lungs/Respiration*
    - Ventilate room.
    - Use air supplied respirator.
- *Clothing*
    - Change clothing as soon as possible.
    - Separate soiled clothing from household laundry.
    - Wash soiled clothing as soon as possible.

Toxic Metals

Toxic metals include antimony, arsenic, barium, beryllium, cadmium, chromium, copper, lead, mercury, nickel, selenium, and thallium.

In general, toxic metals have somewhat uniform health effects. If inhaled they can cause respiratory distress. If ingested they attack the nervous system and kidneys. Cadmium and beryllium serve as examples. Cadmium illustrates the short term effect when AMTs receive massive exposure. Beryllium exposures are less intense but the health effects are initially more subtle. These two metals indicate the range of reactions that can occur from overexposures.

Cadmium

In 1989 the Atlanta, Georgia office of the Occupational Safety and Health Administration (OSHA) had just inspected the landing gear shop of Eastern Airlines. Due to unventilated grinding activities, employees had exposures up to eighty five times the ceiling level for cadmium. Similar overexposures to cadmium exist in other airline maintenance facilities, as well as outside companies performing gear maintenance work for airlines.

Inhalation of cadmium has both acute and chronic effects. Acute effects following inhalation from welding fumes or dust from grinding causes Metal Fume Fever (MFF). Within one day of exposure the AMT develops chills, a fever, shortness of breath, and tiredness. The symptoms look like a viral infection but actually represent a lung reaction. Fortunately the symptoms

of MFF resolve after two days, but severe exposures may progress to more serious disease. At this stage hospitalization is essential.

Chronic low level exposure to cadmium may not immediately produce MFF, but the metal still passes through the lungs into the blood. The red blood cells carry the metal to the liver, kidney, and muscles.

Beryllium

Beryllium, unlike aluminum, is not commonly associated with aircraft. Exposure to beryllium seems unlikely, but review of exposure inspections indicates otherwise. This alloy is present in landing gear bushings and bearing sleeves on aircraft such as the B737. Beryllium exposure is possible even when the metal is a small component of the aircraft.

Beryllium targets the lungs, lymph nodes, and skin either directly or by effecting the immune system. Direct toxicity results from breathing beryllium dust or by skin injuries from handling the ores or metal. The result is pneumonia or dermatitis. Treatment involves removing the individual from the exposure. Few will experience the direct toxicity of this metal. But unlike other metals, Chronic Beryllium Disease (CBD) can develop years after exposure has ceased.

Preventative Actions for Toxic Metal Exposure

- Substitute a less toxic material for the one in use. (For most AMTs this is not practical);
- Implement controls such as local exhaust ventilation to control dust and fumes;
- Do not eat or drink in the workplace;
- Use proper respirators, protective eyewear, and coveralls.

Paints and Primers

Painting can cause a condition known as Occupational Asthma (OA). The culprit is a chemical called diisocyanates which is found in some paints.

Spray painting produces finely atomized particles of paint in the air (over spray), which does not adhere to the object being sprayed. Breathing brings these particles into the lung. The chemicals (diisocyanates) enters the lungs and combines with other proteins forming heavy molecules that affect the body's immune system. The body is now sensitized, but symptoms do not occur and blood tests do not record any change. In other words, there is no evidence of any symptoms or disease. The next time a painter is exposed (weeks, months, or even years), the immune system recognizes the molecule and produces a variety of chemicals that cause an inflammatory reaction. The result is occupational asthma. Estimation is that all adult asthma is work related.

Preventing over spray is the first line of defense. Conventional pressure systems generate forty to fifty psi at the gun resulting in much overspray, whereas there are high volume low pressure systems operating with only 3-5 psi at the gun. If possible, use a high volume paint gun. Using a paint booth is an obvious control measure.

Personal protective equipment is the last step to protect from exposures. Some examples of protective equipment:
- *Negative Pressure Respirators* – for use with primers, dopes and water based paints.
- *Positive Pressure Air Line Respirator* – for use with paints containing diisocyanates.
- *Covering* – Tyvek spraying suit with gloves.
- *Goggles* – When mixing and spraying.

Those who handle dry but not cured painted parts could absorb unbound molecules through their skin. Handling dry painted parts with impermeable gloves and working in well ventilated space also reduces the chances for skin contact with unbound molecules. Preventative measures are clear. Consider others when you are painting.

Hydraulic Fluids
Phosphate ester based hydraulic fluids used in ground equipment and aircraft are available under the trade names Skydrol® and Hyjet®.

Skydrol® is fire resistant hydraulic fluid with a flash point that is much higher than other petroleum based fluid. Passenger airline aircraft must use the fire resistant fluid, while military and general aviation aircraft can use red oil.

Exposure to Skydrol® produces a burning sensation in the eyes and skin. Eye exposure occurs when a geyser of fluid erupts after opening a hydraulic line that is still under pressure. After eye exposure, first aid involves flushing the eye with water. After skin exposure, remove soiled clothing and wash the skin with soap and water. Placing sterile mineral oil in the eye relieves the

burning sensation and pain after flushing the eye with water. Obviously, use of a face shield should be the first line of defense.

Solvents

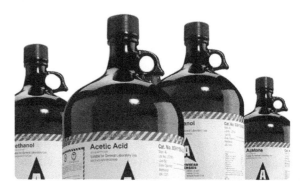

What are solvents? Solvents are liquids or gases that can dissolve or extract other substances. They are used to dissolve grease, oil, and paint; to thin or mix pigments, paint, glue, and epoxy resins; to clean electronics, airplane parts, tools, and engines; and to make other chemicals.

In general, solvents can irritate and damage the skin, eyes, and respiratory system. They cause a narcotic effect on the nervous system and damage internal organs such as the liver and kidneys. These kinds of damage can be acute (from single heavy exposures) or chronic (from repeated low dose exposures over months or years). In addition, some solvents are especially hazardous to specific organs or can cause specific diseases such as cancer.

The most common effect of high level, long term exposure to solvents is the disruption of nerve conduction, resulting in loss of sensations. More severe, but less common is the destruction of the nerves that activate the muscles. Neuropathy is the medical term for this destruction of nerves. Sensory neuropathy causes tingling and loss of feeling in the extremities. Motor neuropathy causes weakness and even paralysis.

Skin Contact
All solvents can dissolve the skin's protective barrier of oils, drying and chapping the skin and causing a kind of dermatitis. In addition, some solvents can cause severe burns and irritation of the skin. Natural solvents such as turpentine and limonene are known to cause skin allergies. Other solvents may cause no symptoms, but may penetrate the skin, enter the bloodstream, travel through the body and damage other organs.

Eyes and Respiratory System

All solvent vapors can irritate and damage the sensitive membranes of the eyes, nose, and throat. Inhaled solvent vapors also can damage lungs. The airborne concentration at which irritation occurs varies from types of solvents. Often workers are unaware of a solvent's effects at low concentrations. Their only symptoms may be increased frequency of colds and respiratory infections. Years of such exposure could lead to chronic lung diseases such as bronchitis. At higher concentrations symptoms are more severe and may include nose bleeds, running eyes, and sore throat. Inhaling high concentrations can lead to severe disorders including pneumonia and death. Liquid solvents splashed in the eyes can quickly cause eye damage.

- **Preventative Actions for Toxic Metal Exposure**
  - Substitute a less toxic material for the one in use. (For most AMTs this is not practical);
  - Implement controls such as local exhaust ventilation to control dust and fumes;
  - Do not eat or drink in the workplace;
  - Use proper respirators, protective eyewear, and coveralls.
- **Preventative Actions for Solvent Exposure**
  - Use personal protective equipment such as a face shield for splash protection, or an impervious apron for protection of your clothes (*Figure 5-2*);
  - Consider the use of a citrus-based cleaner to replace the organic solvent for degreasing; however be sure to check that any product substitution or elimination is consistent with established procedures;
  - Organize your work so cleaning is done at a specific cleaning station, using techniques other than those requiring solvents;
  - Avoid reaching into containers filled with solvent. Instead use pliers to grasp an object in a solvent mixture. Wash parts in cleaning baskets with a handle that extends above the solvent mixture;
  - Use only the smallest quantity of solvent necessary for the job;
  - Cover solvents; don't store containers open to the air;
  - Educate yourself and your staff about skin as a major route of solvent entry into the body. Read and follow the manufacturer's directions. Complaints from coworkers may indicate an overexposure;

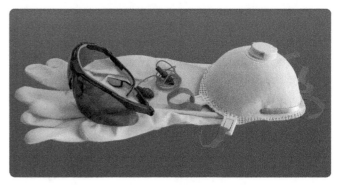

Figure 5-2. Personal protective equipment is the third level of safety.

- Maintain good housekeeping by preventing spills of solvents on work surfaces. Change clothes that become saturated with solvent. Quickly wash skin that contacted solvent liquid;
- Select and issue gloves based on the solvent used. Develop a glove change out schedule. Consult with the glove supplier for specific recommendations. For best protection, use barrier type gloves resistant to the solvent used; double gloving is also possible;
- When exposed to vapors, use half face respirator; if splash protection is necessary use a full face respirator;
- Consult a physician if skin rashes develop while working with solvents.

ILLUMINATION

In order to carry out work safely and efficiently, it is imperative that it be conducted under proper lighting conditions. The cones in the retina of the eye require good light to resolve fine detail. Furthermore, color vision requires adequate light to stimulate the cones. Inappropriate or insufficient lighting can lead to mistakes in work tasks or can increase the time required to do the work.

Illumination refers to the lighting both within the general working environment and also in the locality of the AMT and the task he is carrying out.

The concepts of illumination and luminance are associated with the quantity of light falling on or emanating from a surface, respectively. While it isn't really important to understand all of the mathematical intricacies associated with these concepts, it is helpful to understand the fundamental difference between them.

Illumination is related to the amount of light falling on a surface or an object. The illumination of any point in a facility is dependent on the placement and light output of all light sources that can shine on that point. Luminance is related to the amount of light coming from an object, such as a video display terminal or a wall. Luminance is associated with our subjective impression of brightness.

The source of illuminance is a light of some type. Permanent light sources in facilities are generally fixed to a ceiling or wall. As you move away from these light sources, the intensity of illumination decreases. In fact, it decreases predictably as the square of the distance. If you double the distance between an object and a light source, the illuminance measured at the object drops to one-fourth its previous level. Luminance, on the other hand is associated with the object itself, rather than the relationship between an object and a light source. Our impression of the brightness of an object depends on its luminance. Luminance does not decrease as we move further away from an object, at least within a reasonable range of distances. The reason for this has to do with the way luminance is defined mathematically. At any rate, our experience is that a wall doesn't become less bright simply because we move away from it.

Lighting conditions are considered on maintenance benches, at test stands, on external surfaces of the aircraft, within the aircraft hull, and beneath aircraft wings means that lighting conditions vary dramatically.

An FAA audit of major air carriers included a survey of lighting conditions and found a variety of lighting systems in use, including mercury vapor, metal halide, and high-pressure sodium lights. Although these lights differ in color rendition, the principal problem was with level of illumination.

For work performed on upper and lateral surfaces of the aircraft, illumination levels were deemed adequate. These levels average to 66 foot candles (ft-c) during the day and 51 ft-c for night maintenance work. For work conducted below wings, inside the fuselage, and in cargo areas, illumination is poor and use of supplemental lighting systems was noted. However, these frequently were placed too far from the work being performed and were too few in number. The result was that illumination levels in shielded regions ranged, on occasion, to 10-14 ft-c. In terms of recommended minimum illumination levels for aircraft repair and inspection tasks established by the Illuminating Engineering Society, these levels are not adequate. A minimum level of 75 ft-c is recommended for repair tasks. (*Table 5-1*)

CLIMATE AND TEMPERATURE

Humans can work within quite a wide range of temperatures and climatic conditions, but performance is adversely affected at extremes. As can be seen in *Figure 5-3*, when it is either too cold and wet or too hot and humid, performance diminishes.

PHYSICAL ENVIRONMENT

GUIDANCE FOR RECOMMENDED LIGHT LEVELS IN VARIOUS WORKSPACES	
Activity	Illumination (lux, lumen/m2)
Public areas with dark surroundings.	20–50
Simple orientation for short visits.	50–100
Working areas where visual tasks are only occasionally performed.	100–150
Warehouses, Homes, Theaters, Archives	150
Easy Office Work, Classes	250
Normal Office Work, PC Work, Study Library, Groceries, Show Rooms, Laboratories	500
Supermarkets, Mechanical Workshops, Office Landscapes	750
Normal Drawing Work, Detailed Mechanical Workshops, Operation Theaters	1 000
Detailed Drawing Work, Very Detailed Mechanical Works	1 500–2 000
Performance of visual tasks of low contrast and very small size for prolonged periods of time.	2 000–5 000
Performance of very prolonged and exacting visual tasks.	5 000–10 000
Performance of very special visual tasks of extremely low contrast and small size.	10 000–20 000

Table 5-1. Recommendations for task related light levels.

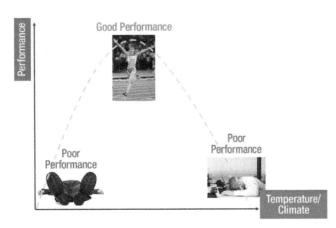

Figure 5-3. The relationship between climate, temperature and performance.

AMTs routinely work both within the hangar and outside. Exposure to the widest range of temperature and climate is likely to be encountered outdoors, in direct summer sun, strong winds, heavy rain, high humidity, or in the depths of winter. Although hangars exclude inclement weather, they can be cold and drafty, especially if the hangar doors have to remain open.

On summer days the structure of the airplane can magnify heat and its effects. Environmental factors that influence the body's heat load include the ambient temperature, radiant heat, and air velocity. Hot tarmacs will also radiate heat. Small work areas within the fuselage, wing area, and other structures create a micro environment much different from the outside. Taken to extremes, this heat load can kill.

THE BODY'S RESPONSE TO HEAT

To function efficiently, the body needs a stable internal temperature which is a balance between heat production and loss. Under normal circumstances 65% of the body's heat loss is by passive transfer (radiation) and 20% by evaporation. Passive heat loss is entirely sufficient to remove this heat load, and the body's temperature remains constant.

The body's primary defense against overheating is sweating which produces heat loss through evaporation. Concurrently, vessels in the skin dilate to bring more blood from the inner body to the skin; the effect is similar to a radiator. Dilation and evaporation can prevent the elevation of the body's core temperature.

As temperature increases, both radiation and evaporation become less effective. With temperatures exceeding 99°F, (37.2°C) the body gains radiant heat from the environment. At 100% humidity, evaporation is ineffective. High humidity occurs not only because of climatic changes, but when clothes absorb sweat and prevent evaporation. Under these circumstances, it is difficult to maintain a stable body temperature.

Heat Stress and Major Disorders

Five major disorders arise from excessive heat exposure. The first and most serious is heat stroke. Fortunately, aviation maintenance activities rarely lead to heat stroke. Closely related to heat stroke is heat exhaustion, caused by prolonged exposure to heat without adequate salt and water intake. Thirst, nausea, weakness, and confusion are common symptoms. Treatment usually involves intravenous hydration. One day in the hospital should be expected because without proper treatment heat exhaustion can lead to stroke.

The other three disorders, heat cramps, heat syncope, and heat rash are less serious but more common. Heat cramps are painful muscle spasms that occur after performing strenuous activities and create severe spasms (lasting one to three minutes) among the muscles employed. While the skin is moist and cool, the underlying muscles feel like hard stony lumps. Treatment requires moving to a cool environment and drinking a salt solution. Drinking commercially available electrolyte replacement liquids is effective in replenishing the lost sodium that causes the cramps. It is advised to miss one to three days of work after such an event.

Heat syncope is the sudden loss of consciousness due to dilation of blood vessels in the skin, but does not involve the loss of blood flow to the brain that occurs in heat stroke. The skin is cool and moist and the pulse is weak, with a systolic blood pressure of less than 100mm HG. Treatment involves moving the victim to a cool environment and having him/her lie down. In this reclined position, the victim of heat syncope rapidly regains consciousness and can take liquids by mouth. It is advised to miss one day of work following such an event.

Heat rash, commonly called prickly heat, is a common skin problem in hot environments. Manifestation of heat rash are red papules which usually appear in the trunk and groin (not the palms and soles) where sweat cannot evaporate. The papules itch and can become infected. Treatment involves reducing sweat production by moving to cool environments, where the person should remain for about one week.

Heat Index (HI) is the temperature that the body feels when heat and humidity combine. The HI is a good predictor of when heat stress will produce a heat related illness. (*Table 5-2*)

Understanding how the body maintains a constant internal temperature permits for implementation of both company wide operating policies and individual responsibilities aimed at preventing heat related disorders. Preventing heat related illnesses requires appropriate control of the environment, combined with an individual's knowledgeable in physiological responses to heat.

Working in the Cold

The popular concept is that aviation people work in warm, cozy hangars. In fact, hangars are poorly heated and drafty and repairs are sometimes outside on the flight line. Add the chilly winds of winter and conditions are ideal for producing adverse effects on the body. The medical term for low body temperature is hypothermia. Since normal body temperature is 98.6°F (37°C) and outside temperatures usually are lower, hypothermia is a relative term. Hypothermia can occur at temperatures above freezing. (*Table 5-3*) It is evident that cold (or cool) airplanes set the stage for hypothermia.

THE BODY'S RESPONSE TO COLD

To function effectively, the body's metabolic processes maintain a constant temperature of approximately 98.6°F (37°F) with minor variation. Heat loss originates from three processes. The first is evaporation of sweat, causing cooling. The second is conductive heat loss, or the transfer of heat from a warm object (the hand) to a cold object (a tool). The third source of heat loss is convection, also known as wind chill. Protecting against the cold involves limiting the loss of body heat by these processes.

The body is a heat engine, so any loss of heat triggers physiological responses to maintain body temperature. The body's first response to heat loss is generation of more heat through a violent and uncontrolled muscle

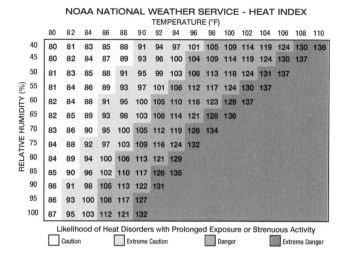

Table 5-2. Heat Index predicts likelihood of heat related disorders.

Table 5-3. Cold related symptoms can occur above freezing.

contraction called shivering. This well known sign is an early indication of heat loss. As body temperature continues to drop, the shivering becomes less violent and eventually stops. The next response is constriction of the blood vessels, called vasoconstriction which reduces blood flow to the extremities. The net effect is the shunting of blood from the extremities, such as the fingers and toes, to the warmer organs of the body's core. A significant temperature difference now exists between the extremities and the core.

The physiological response to cold results in observable symptoms (*Table 5-4*), most notably in the fingers and toes. Vasoconstriction results in redness, or in some areas paleness. Prolonged cold exposure can result in an extremity becoming swollen or blistered, forcing movement to become clumsy. Sloughing and scaling of skin in the exposed area occurs with numbness and tingling.

SYMPTOMS FROM OVEREXPOSURE TO COLD
1. Redness or extreme paleness in exposed area.
2. Pain in exposed area, which lead to symptoms in #1.
3. Blisters filled with clear fluid or blood after cold exposure.
4. Difficulty moving areas of exposed skin, clumsiness, poor control of fingers.
5. Scaling and sloughing on the skin following cold exposure.
6. Blackening of skin and loss of movement in exposed areas.
7. Numbness and tingling in exposed areas.

Table 5-4. Physiological response to cold.

In the extreme situation, continued loss of heat can be greater than the body's ability to replace it. Not only are the extremities cold, but core temperature begins to drop. Heart rate slows down, reducing distribution of warm body fluids to tissues, and the extremities become numb. When ambient temperatures are below freezing, frostbite (actual freezing of tissues) starts at the tip of the nose or fingers. Tissue injury becomes irreversible, and eventual death results from cardiac arrest.

The work environment focuses the AMTs attention to the job at hand rather than on the early, subtle symptoms of exposure to the cold. Perhaps the job involves a fuel system repair so that fingers, hands, and even clothes become wet with fuel. Evaporating fuel lowers the skin temperature at the same time that vasoconstriction is shunting warm blood away from the extremity.

Symptoms such as those outlined in *Table 5-4* may progress beyond those early warning signs. Clumsiness on the job may be a manifestation of cold exposure. The solution requires immediate warmth to the extremities. Remember, local effects of cold do not require temperatures below freezing. The effects occur because of a temperature difference between the body's core and the unprotected extremity.

KNOW YOUR TEMPERATURES

The stage is set for hypothermia when heat loss occurs faster than the body can generate it. Contact with water promotes heat loss 25–30 times faster than with air. Water contact not only includes a drenching rain but also perspiration. Another risk factor is wind speed. *Table 5-3* illustrates the combined effect of ambient temperature with wind speed on the times it takes for skin to freeze. Cold related symptoms (*Table 5-4*)

usually occur slowly, as the environmental conditions depicted in *Table 5-3* show, thus gradually overcome the body's ability to replace heat.

PREVENTING COLD RELATED DISORDERS

Loss of heat not only causes injury and reduces productivity, but also results in careless mistakes. Follow the recommendations in *Table 5-5* to maintain body heat and productivity. The benefits of the first two recommendations (education about cold exposure and access to a warm shelter) can easily be overlooked or taken for granted. Think about and discuss cold exposures with coworkers, even before the first cold weather. This discussion should also include an inventory of the break room for the availability of warm beverages (more than just coffee).

RECOMMENDATIONS FOR WORKING IN THE COLD
1. Educate all employees about the risks of cold exposure and develop appropriate preventative strategies for each task.
2. Provide a warm shelter, out of the elements, preferably one supplied with warm beverages.
3. Reduce activities that promote heavy sweating.
4. Preserve manual dexterity by using hand warmers, gloves and frequent breaks to a warm shelter.
5. Apply emollient or moisturizer to the hands regularly, especially if you come in contact with fluids.
6. Use nonconductive tools to prevent frostbite to hands.
7. Require appropriate protective clothing when exposed to the elements.
8. Discourage the use of alcohol to keep warm.
9. Use the buddy system to observe evidence of cold injury or impairment.

Table 5-5. Preventing cold related disorders.

Because sweating produces evaporative heat loss, recommendation #3 suggests to reduce activities that generate heavy sweating. Outdoor workers whose jobs require high energy expenditures comply with this recommendation by pacing their work. Sweating may also occur because of work around a hot engine in an enclosed test cell. If this job requires working outdoors, the potential exists for cold stress due to evaporative heat loss. (Hot followed by cold exposure is unusual, since most aircraft repair requires static postures such as sitting, standing or kneeling.)

To preserve manual dexterity, the hand must receive a constant supply of warm blood. Shunting of blood away from the extremities reduces dexterity, causes mistakes, slows down production, and ultimately creates errors in maintenance.

Hand warmers, gloves of acceptable thickness, and breaks in a warm shelter (recommendation #4) counter the effect of vasoconstriction. In addition to manipulating small objects, aircraft repair requires contact with fluids, especially fuels with low vapor pressure. As these fuels evaporate, evaporative heat loss and drying occur, usually from the fingers. As solvents and fuels also dissolve the fats that make the skin pliable, dry skin results which frequently cracks at the edges of the fingernails. The low environmental humidity associated with cold weather also enhances the irritability of the skin. To restore moisture, AMTs should frequently apply emollients (recommendation #5) that soften and soothe irritated skin. Generously apply these creams to the lips, backs of the hands, and tips of fingers. These areas are more vulnerable to drying than the wrists and palms. Most basic stores are well stocked with products commonly labeled as moisturizers, emollients, or hand creams.

Conductive heat loss occurs when the warm hand touches a cold object such as a tool or the surface of a cold aircraft. The answer to this problem is to wear gloves or use a tool with a nonconductive handle (recommendation #6). Wrapping nonconductive tape around the handle of a tool is an easy method of reducing conductive heat loss.

When it comes to protective clothing, recommendation #7 emphasizes three layers. The outer layer serves as a windbreaker, while the middle layer provides insulation and is generally made of wool, down or a synthetic pile. The inner layer, usually made of cotton or a synthetic weave, permits the escape of moisture. Protective clothing is especially important for those who work on the flight line. Moisture enhances heat loss, so wet clothing should be changed as soon as possible. Having an extra pair of socks and trousers on hand is a good idea.

Do not use alcohol to maintain body temperature (recommendation #8), because alcohol actually increases heat loss, not to mention the risk of losing your job.

When working in a cold environment, encourage use of the buddy system (Recommendation #9). Observe your buddy for signs of cold exposure such as clumsiness or shivering. Also, recognize that working in the cold reduces productivity, so the buddy system provides assistance in completing a job and making sure it is carried out correctly.

AMTs cannot be expected to maintain the rigorous standards expected in their profession in all types of environmental conditions. EASA Part-145 Acceptable Means of Compliance (AMC) 145.25(c) requires that environmental conditions be adequate for work to be carried out, stating:

"The working environment for line maintenance should be such that the particular maintenance or inspection task can be carried out without undue distraction. It therefore follows that where the working environment deteriorates to an unacceptable level in respect of temperature, moisture, hail, ice, snow, wind, light, dust/ other airborne contamination, the particular maintenance or inspection tasks should be suspended until satisfactory conditions are reestablished."

Unfortunately, as pressure to turn aircraft around rapidly means that some maintenance tasks are not put off until the conditions are more conducive to work. In that case, follow the recommendations listed.

MOTION AND VIBRATION

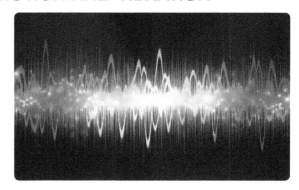

AMTs often make use of staging and mobile access platforms to reach various parts of an aircraft. As these get higher, they tend to become less stable. For example when working at height on a scissors platform or 'cherry picker', applying force to a bolt being fixed to the aircraft may cause the platform to move away from the aircraft. The extent to which this occurs does not just depend on the height of the platform, but its design and serviceability. Any sensation of unsteadiness may distract an AMT, as he/she may concentrate more on keeping balance than the task. Furthermore, it is vitally important that AMTs use mobile access platforms properly in order to avoid serious injury.

Vibration in aviation maintenance is usually associated with the use of rotating or percussive tools and equipment, such as generators. Low frequency noise, such as that associated with aircraft engines, can also cause vibration. Vibration between 0.5 Hz to 20 Hz is most problematic, as the human body absorbs most of the vibratory energy in this range. The range between 50–150 Hz is most troublesome for the hand and is associated with vibratory-induced White Finger Syndrome (VWF). Pneumatic tools can produce troublesome vibrations in this range and frequent use can lead to reduced local blood flow and pain associated with VWF. Vibration can be annoying, possibly disrupting an AMTs concentration.

WORKING ENVIRONMENT

The work environment should be positive and promote a strong safety culture.

WHAT IS A SAFETY CULTURE?
A safety culture is one where there is a shared value for the importance of safety. Each worker, from the top to the bottom, must be able to articulate their specific contributions to safety.

Building a Safety Culture
Safety culture requires time to develop. It needs a proactive approach from all personnel if it is to grow. A long lasting culture will only flourish when good safety behaviors are actively encouraged, while poor safety behaviors are viewed as unprofessional and dealt with accordingly. All members must see safety and professionalism as "the way we do business", and these

views need to be internalized and demonstrated by management and all coworkers. A working environment with a positive safety culture includes:

- A safe physical environment that considers health and safety seriously (discussed throughout this *Sub-Module*);
- A positive social environment with excellent communication and promotes individual and team responsibility (discussed in *Sub-Module 03*);
- A workplace that focuses on tasks that need to be carried out (discussed in *Sub-Module 06*).

CONCLUSION
Aircraft maintenance requires all three components of the working environment to be managed carefully in order to achieve a safe and efficient system. It is important to recognize that AMTs are typically highly professional and pragmatic in their outlook, and generally attempt to do the best work possible regardless of their working conditions. Favorable maintenance organizations do their best to support this dedication by providing the necessary environment for a safe and efficient workplace.

Question: 5-1
What should happen if noise can not be eliminated to protect hearing?

Question: 5-4
Five major disorders arise from heat exposure. What are they?

Question: 5-2
What are some of the dangerous substances that AMTs are exposed to?

Question: 5-5
Heat loss originates from what three processes?

Question: 5-3
What are some of the ways that solvents can enter your system and cause damage?

Question: 5-6
A positive safety culture includes?

ANSWERS

Answer: 5-1

Selecting some form of Personal Protective Equipment in the form of hearing protection such as ear plugs or full ear muffs.

Answer: 5-2

Carbon Monoxide (CO)
- Kerosene based fuel
- Toxic Metals
- Paints and Primers
- Hydraulic Fluids
- Solvents

Answer: 5-3

Solvents can be absorbed through the skin, through the eyes and through the respiratory system.

Answer: 5-4

Heat Stroke – The most serious, but fortunately rare for AMTs;
- Heat exhaustion
- Heat cramps
- Heat syncope
- Heat rash

Answer: 5-5

- Evaporation of sweat;
- Conductive heat loss (the transfer of heat from a warm object - hand, to a cold object - tool);
- Convection, known as wind chill.

Answer: 5-6

- A safe physical environment that considers health and safety;
- A positive social environment with excellent communication;
- A workplace that focuses on tasks that need to be carried out;
- A shared value for the importance of safety.

PART-66 SYLLABUS LEVELS

CERTIFICATION CATEGORY →

	B1	B2

Sub-Module 06

TASKS

Knowledge Requirements

9.6 - Tasks

	B1	B2
Physical work; Repetitive tasks; Visual inspection; Complex systems.	1	1

TASKS

9.6 - TASKS

INTRODUCTION

Not all Aircraft Maintenance Technicians (AMTs) are generalists. Many specialize in the tasks they carry out, for example as either an airframe, powerplant, or an avionics specialist. When working within an organization, an AMT will also be sent on 'type courses'. These courses provide the requisite skills and knowledge to carry out tasks on specific type of equipment.

Most aircraft maintenance involves replacing and repairing unserviceable parts, AMTs can not always plan for every situation, but most activities do involve prior knowledge so that parts, materials, tools and other equipment can be prearranged before the task is started.

PLANNING OF TASKS, EQUIPMENT, AND SPARES

Planning is critical to making good decisions. It ensures there are qualified personnel, tools, equipment, material, maintenance data, and facilities at the right place, at the right time, for the scheduled and, (as much as possible) unscheduled tasks.

Planning should therefore include having knowledge about what relevant resources are available in case they are required. Decisions made in a maintenance environment may be influenced by access to replacement parts and support equipment, or at least being able to obtain them in a timely manner.

AMTs sometimes find that a part may need further attention, but may decide to defer it if they knew a replacement is not readily available.

Sometimes AMTs may find themselves in a situation where task completion is perceived as the prime objective, but a lack of required supporting data, facilities, tooling, and equipment may mean it is not possible to complete the task by the book. In these situations, violations or workaround are more likely to occur particularly when the manufacturers' required spares are not available to perform the task. Routine violations may become the norm within an organization, or even the habits of an individual, usually because people believe that the rules are too rigid or unnecessary. These routine violations typically occur during the performance of simple maintenance tasks.

The following case study illustrates the danger of deciding to employ workarounds.

Lack of resources... not a problem!

When the flight crew of a B747 passenger aircraft checked in for their evening's flight, they were informed that there was a known problem with the 4L main entry door, but the engineers responsible were confident that the aircraft would be declared serviceable at or near the scheduled departure time. This proved to be the case and the aircraft's flight engineer checked the door for satisfactory operation himself. Due to a recent history of problems with this door, the cabin crew stationed at the door were briefed to monitor it after takeoff and keep the flight deck informed of any changes.

Shortly after takeoff, during the initial climb, the door handle moved from the 3 o'clock closed position to the 1 o'clock partially-open position. The nominated cabin crew notified the flight deck and as a precaution the crew decided to return to the departure airport.

During pressure testing on the ground, engineers found that the door handle moved towards the unlock position. After comparison with another door, they discovered that the upper torque tube had been replaced recently during troubleshooting for a previous defect. It was discovered that the upper torque tube had been drilled in such a way that there was an incorrect angular relationship between two sets of holes in it. When the replacement torque tube was compared with the failed one, it was found that the axis of the bell crank bolt holes had been drilled with approximately 18 degrees of circumferential displacement from their required correct position, resulting in the door being rigged incorrectly.

The first report of problems with the door had been made several days earlier, and resulted in the discovery of a broken torque tube and latch crank. A replacement tube and crank assembly were ordered. There was a shortage of certifying staff and an appropriate Licensed Aircraft Maintenance Engineer (LAME) had to be called in on overtime. When the LAME arrived at 2100, he was briefed by the shift lead. The new torque tube arrived at 0030, and was found to be 'undrilled'. The aircraft maintenance manual called for a drill jig, which allows for the holes to be drilled precisely. However, the drill jig was not available, and the machining workshops were closed for the night. The LAME and the shift lead decided to drill the tube in the local hanger workshop due to time constraints and the operational requirements for the aircraft.

Rigging of the door began at approximately 0230 and continued for three hours. The team was fatigued by this time, and so the decision was made to hand the task over to the incoming day shift. As the day shift LAME was not available, a verbal handover was made to one of the two available day shift engineers assigned to complete the task.

Later, another qualified LAME was tasked with coordinating the activity on the door in addition to his other work. The door was later inspected by the LAME, who considered that all the maintenance manual requirements had been met. The door was then reassembled, and the aircraft was released for service at 1700 the next day. However, there were continued problems with the door culminating in the incident.

When the drilling error became apparent, another torque tube was obtained and drilled off in the machine workshops using a vertical milling machine. The door was subsequently reassembled and rigged with no problems. The aircraft was returned to service with no further door problems since being reported.

What would you do?

During a routine inspection you discover a control linkage rod end is worn and has significant free play. This type of linkage is prone to wear on this type of aircraft, hence the regularity of the specific inspection.

A check of the limitations in the manufacturer's manual indicates it is at the limit of (but still within) allowable wear. Knowing the aircraft will be operated extensively after your check, and considering it is at the limit after a second check, you decide to replace the part.

After checking with the hangar storeman, you discover this part is not in stock, and a replacement is a week away. Considering that when checking the wear twice it was at the allowable maximum and a replacement is not available, you now change your mind.

Is this your preferred decision?

Referring back to dealing with uncertainty, what else could you do? Going back to the questions you could ask yourself:

> *Are the present conditions drifting towards the boundaries of safe operation?*

You could gather more data on proposed aircraft usage, wear rates and system tolerances to assure yourself that it will remain functional until a replacement is available.

> *What conditions are within my ability (or authority) to influence?*

You cannot get a replacement part so you can either accept the present condition of the component or place it unserviceable. In deciding which option to take ask yourself:

> *Regardless of organizational stresses and conditions, what do I need to do to ensure the safety of aircraft that I, my colleagues, or my organization work on?*

In answering this question; if you can state that the component is still within tolerance and will be operated under normal conditions, while it might have been beneficial to replace it at the present time, the aircraft will still be operating within safe boundaries until a replacement is available. This would reduce your level of uncertainty and ensure that you had made a fully informed decision based on as much information as possible and considering all of the possible consequences.

KEY POINTS

- Decision making is a critical skill in aviation maintenance.
- The process of decision making includes: defining the problem, considering the options, selecting and implementing the options available; and reviewing the outcome.
- The need to make a decision to address a problem or unexpected situation can bring with it added situational issues, such as stress and time pressure.
- Decisions should be informed; that is they should be made based on all the required information available.

Blindly starting a task without planning how best to do it is almost certainly the best way to invite problems. Before commencing a task, an individual, team, or planner should ask themselves a number of questions.

These may include:
- Do I know exactly what the task is that has to be done?
- Are the following resources available to do it effectively and accurately within the time permitted?
  - Personnel;
  - Equipment/spares;
  - Documentation, information and guidance;
  - Facilities such as hangar space, lighting, etc.
- Do I or we have the skills and proficiency necessary to complete the task?

Information about specific tasks should be detailed on job cards or task sheets. These will indicate the task (e.g. checks or inspection, repair, replacement, overhaul) and other details that will assist the AMT. If there is any doubt what needs to be done, written guidance material is the best resource. Coworkers may unintentionally give incorrect or imprecise direction.

It is generally the shift supervisor's job to ensure that the resources are available for staff to carry out tasks. It is likely that, within a shift or a team, various sub tasks are allocated to individuals by the supervisor.

Management has the responsibility to ensure staff have suitable training. It is ultimately the individual who needs to decide whether he/she has the necessary skills and experience to do what is assigned.

PHYSICAL WORK

AMTs have a relatively active occupation. Regardless of the job being done, most tasks tend to have elements of fine motor control, requiring precision as well as activities requiring strength and gross manipulation.

From a biomechanical perspective, the human body is a series of physical links (bones) connected at certain points (joints) that allow various movements. Muscles provide the motive force for all movements, both fine and gross. This is known as the musculoskeletal system. The force that can be applied in any given posture is dependent on the strength available from muscles and the mechanical advantage provided by the relative positions of the load, muscle connections, and joints.

As the AMT gets older the musculoskeletal system stiffens and muscles become weaker, injuries become more likely and take longer to heal. Obesity limits the physical spaces that can be accessed. Staying in shape will minimize the effects of aging, and can help make sure that normal weight can be maintained.

Recent awareness of Latent Medical and Environmental Conditions (LMEC), it is now recognized that the tasks on aircraft need to be within the physical limitations of the AMT. Boeing uses a computerized tool, based on human performance data (body sizes, strengths, leverages, pivots, etc.), to ensure that modern aircraft are designed such that the majority of AMTs will be able to access aircraft equipment, and apply the necessary strength to loosen or tighten objects, etc. (*also known as Ease of Maintainability*).

Clearly we are all different in terms of physical stature and strength and as a consequence, our physical limitations vary. Attempting to lift a heavy object which is beyond our physical capability is likely to lead to injury. The use of tools generally make tasks easier, and can make tasks that were once outside of our physical powers attainable.

Physical work over a period of time will result in fatigue. This is normally not a problem if there is adequate rest and recovery time between work periods. It can however, become a problem if the body is not allowed to recover, possibly leading to illness or injuries. Hence, AMTs should try to take breaks.

Missing a break in an effort to get a job done within a certain time frame can be counterproductive, as fatigue diminishes motor skills, perception, awareness and standards. As a consequence, work may slow and mistakes may occur that need to be rectified. The physical fitness of the AMT should match the task that is assigned.

REPETITIVE TASKS

People tend to become complacent with practiced tasks.

Repetitive tasks can be tedious and boring. Most of the human factors research associated with repetitive tasks have been carried out in manufacturing environments where workers carry out the same action many times a minute. This does not generally apply to aviation maintenance technicians.

Repetitive tasks for AMTs typically refer to tasks that are performed several times during a shift, or a number of times during a short time period. An example of this would be the checking life jackets on an aircraft during daily inspections.

AMTs may specialize in a certain aspect of maintenance, such as engines which can result in similar tasks being required several times a day.

The main danger with repetitive tasks is that of complacency. For example, one may become so practiced that they may cease to consult the manual, or to use job cards. If something about a task is changed, they may not be aware of the change. Also steps may be skipped, or failed to be given due attention, especially if it is to check something which is rarely found to be wrong, damaged, or out of tolerance. This applies particularly to visual inspection.

Making assumptions along the lines of 'Oh I've done that job dozens of times!' can occur even if a task has not been undertaken for some time. It is always advisable to be wary of changes to procedures or parts, remembering that 'Success breeds complacency. Complacency breeds failure'.

VISUAL INSPECTION

Visual inspection is one of the primary methods employed during maintenance to ensure the aircraft remains in an airworthy condition. The Aloha accident referenced in Chapter 1 highlights what can happen when visual inspection is poor. Visual inspection can be described as the process of using the eye, alone or in conjunction with various aids to examine and evaluate the condition of systems or components of an aircraft.

AMTs may use magnifiers and boroscopes to enhance their visual capabilities. Visual inspection may be assisted by examining the element using other senses (touch, hearing, smell, etc.). Also manipulating the element being inspected helps to make further judgments about its condition. For instance, feeling a surface for unevenness, or pushing against an object to look for any unanticipated movement. Good eyesight is of prime importance in visual inspection. This calls for glasses or contact lenses to be used where prescribed and regular eyesight checks to be scheduled.

Although vision is important, it is extremely important that good judgments are concluded about what is seen. To do this, training, experience and common sense are called for. Reliable visual inspection requires that the AMT first sees the defect and then actually recognizes that it is a defect. This comes with practice, but experienced coworkers can pass on known tell tale signs of what to look for.

Technical bulletins are important as they prepare an AMT for known and potential defects. The AMT should thus keep current on these pertinent bulletins. For example, blue staining on an aircraft fuselage may be considered insignificant at first sight, but information from a technical bulletin of 'blue ice' and external toilet leaks may alert one a more serious problem. There are various steps that can be taken to carry out reliable visual inspection such as:

- Understanding the area, component or system that is being inspected (as specified on the work card);
- Making sure the environment is conducive to the visual inspection (lighting, physical access);
- Conducting a systematic visual search, moving ones eyes carefully in a set pattern so that all parts are inspected;
- Examining thoroughly any potential degradation or defect that is seen and deciding whether it constitutes a problem;
- Recording a problem that is found and continuing the search a few steps prior to where one left off.

Visual inspection requires a considerable amount of concentration. Long spells of continuous inspection can be tedious and result in low arousal. Low arousal or lack of motivation can contribute to a failure to spot a potential problem or a failure in recognizing a defect during visual inspection. The effects are potentially worse when an inspector has a very low expectation of finding a defect, such as on a new aircraft.

AMTs may find it beneficial to take short breaks between discrete visual inspection tasks, such as at a particular system component, frame, lap joint, etc. This is much better than pausing midway through an inspection. Finally, Non-Destructive Inspection (NDI) includes an element of visual inspection, but usually permits detection of defects below visual thresholds. Various specialist tools are used for this purpose, such as the use of eddy currents and Fluorescent Penetrant Inspection (FPI).

COMPLEX SYSTEMS

All large modern aircraft can be described as complex systems. Within these aircraft, there are a myriad of separate systems, many of which themselves may be considered complex, e.g. flying controls, landing gear, air conditioning, flight management computers. *Table 6-1* gives an example of the breadth of complexity in aircraft systems.

Any complex system can be thought of as having a wide variety of inputs. The system typically performs complex modifications on these inputs, or the inputs may trigger complex responses. There may be a single output, or many distributed outputs from the system.

The purpose, composition, and function of a simple system is usually easily understood by an AMT. Fault finding and diagnosis should be relatively simple with such systems (although appropriate manuals etc., should be referred to where necessary). With a complex system, it should still be clear to an AMT what the system's purpose is. However, its composition and function may be harder to conceptualize.

To maintain such complex systems, specific training is needed with an understanding of how the system works (and how it can fail), what it is made up of, and which components can fail. It is important to understand enough about the overall functioning of a large complex aircraft, but not so much that one becomes overwhelmed by its complexity. Thus, system specific training must achieve the correct balance between detailed system knowledge and analytical troubleshooting skills.

With complex systems within aircraft, written procedures and reference material become an even more important source of guidance than with simple systems. They may describe comprehensively the method of performing maintenance tasks, such as inspections, adjustments, and tests. They may describe the relationship of one system to other systems and often most importantly, provide cautions or bring attention to specific areas or components. It is important to follow the procedures to the letter, since deviations from procedures may have implication on other parts of the system.

TYPE OF AILERON	NATURE OF SYSTEM
Simple Aileron	Direct connection from control column to control surface; direct movement.
Servo Tab Aileron	Direct connection from control column to servo tab; aerodynamic movement of surface.
Powered Aileron	Connection from control column to servo valve via input; hydraulic movement of surface; feedback mechanism; position indication.
Powered Aileron/Roll Spoiler	As above but with interface to spoiler input system to provide additional roll capability.
Fly-By-Wire Aileron System	No connection from control column to surface. Electrical command signal to electro-hydraulic servo valve on actuator; signal modified and limited by intermediate influence of flight control computer.

Table 6-1. Example of increasing complexity—the aileron system.

When working with complex systems, it is important to make reference to appropriate guidance material. This typically breaks down the system conceptually or physically, making it easier to understand and work on.

In modern aircraft, it is likely that the expertise to maintain a complex system may be distributed among a team. Thus, avionic technicians and mechanical technicians may need to work in concert to examine completely a system that has an interface to the pilot in the cockpit (such as undercarriage controls, and indications).

A single modern aircraft is complex enough, but many AMTs are qualified on several types and variants of aircraft. This will usually mean that there is less opportunity to become familiar with one type, making it even more important to stick to the prescribed procedures and refer to the reference manual wherever necessary. There is a particular vulnerability where tasks are very similar between a number of different aircraft (e.g. spoiler systems on the Airbus 320, Boeing 757 and Boeing 767), and may be more easily confused if no reference is made to the manual.

CONCLUSION

Human error is avoidable when attention is given to the following:

- Before a task is to be completed, plan ahead by making sure all resources needed are on hand. Having the proper resources, (people, tools, equipment, spare parts) are paramount in error avoidance.
- Being aware of the physical space and ability to physically complete the job in a comfortable manner, also will make sure that discomfort, fatigue, exhaustion do not contribute to human error.
- Not allowing complacency when performing repetitive tasks can also create an error free environment.
- Knowing what steps can be taken to avoid error in carrying out visual inspection.
- Paying attention, planning, awareness will contribute to an error free tasks.

Question: 6-1

Planning for planned and unplanned tasks involves making sure which resources are available?

Question: 6-2

What is the main concern of repetitive tasks?

Question: 6-3

What are two ways the AMT can help during visual inspection?

Question: 6-4

Where can you find information on performing specific tasks?

Question: 6-5

Success breeds complacency, what does complacency breed?

ANSWERS

Answer: 6-1
Qualified personnel;
Tools and equipment;
Documentation;
Facilities such as hangar space and lighting.

Answer: 6-4
Information can be attained on specific tasks from job cards or task sheets.

Answer: 6-2
The main danger with performing repetitive tasks is complacency. If something is changed, failure to consult the manual or job card may arise.

Answer: 6-5
Complacency breeds failure.

Answer: 6-3
The use of magnifiers or boroscopes;
Using other sensors such as touch, hearing, smell.

HUMAN FACTORS

COMMUNICATION

SUB-MODULE 07

PART-66 SYLLABUS LEVELS

CERTIFICATION CATEGORY →

	B1	B2

Sub-Module 07

COMMUNICATION

Knowledge Requirements

9.7 - Communication

	B1	B2
Within and between teams; Work logging and recording; Keeping up to date, currency; Dissemination of information.	1	1

9.7 - COMMUNICATION

INTRODUCTION

WHAT IS COMMUNICATION?

Communication can be defined as achieving shared meaning, and to be effective requires four elements working together.

- The individual sending the message must present that message clearly, with the necessary detail, and should have credibility.
- The person receiving the message must be prepared to, and decide to, listen, ask questions if they don't understand something, and trust the person sending the message.
- The delivery method chosen must suit the circumstances and needs of both sender and receiver.
- The content of the message has to resonate and connection some level with the already held beliefs of the receiver.
- If communication is to be effective, therefore, it has to be worked upon and refined.

COMMUNICATION CHANNELS

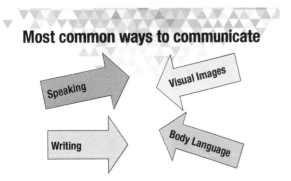

When we think of communication, we tend to think first of oral/spoken communication, but in the maintenance environment, as elsewhere, communication takes place via several channels, not just the spoken word.

Maintenance is heavily reliant on documentation for information transfer; for example, logbooks, maintenance manuals and parts catalog. However, important information is also transferred via other means, over the phone, via face to face communication, and even through body language and other Non-verbal cues. Communication in maintenance also occurs via physical cues such as the placement of tools and parts and the location of ground servicing equipment, tags or lockout devices. In some cases we consciously transmit or seek information, such as signing off a logbook entry, or referring to a maintenance manual. In other cases, however, we are still sending or receiving information without necessarily being aware that communication is occurring.

The main communication channels in maintenance can be summarized as oral–speech; written–documentation; Non-verbal–wordless cues; and physical cues.

Speech
Speaking is the most natural form of communication, yet oral communication is often far from perfect. The error rate for oral communication in industrial settings is estimated to be around 3 per cent. In other words, approximately one out of every 30 spoken exchanges in workplaces involves a misunderstanding! In aviation, such communication errors can be catastrophic.

In 1989, a 747 freighter crashed into terrain when air traffic control told the pilot to 'descend two-four-zero-zero', meaning 2400ft, but the pilot interpreted this as an instruction to descend to 400ft. Whenever oral communication occurs in maintenance, those conveying the message need to make sure the message has been understood, and those receiving it must listen, confirm that they have received the message, and ask questions if they have any doubts.

Documents
Maintenance is driven by paperwork. Communicating via documentation is such a part of the job many, AMTs spend more time wielding a pen than they do a spanner or screwdriver. Communication via written material usually means there are few opportunities to clarify or query the message once it is 'sent'.

In the English language, many words can have more than one meaning. Generally, this is a strength for the richness of the language, but for aviation maintenance, a potential problem. For example, in everyday English the word 'tap' has several different meanings, including: a tap above a sink, the action of removing fluid from something, to listen in on a telephone conversation, or to hit/strike gently.

The European Association of Aerospace Industries has developed a form of simplified English to create brief and unambiguous text for aerospace manuals, and both Boeing and Airbus are now using the system. Simplified English limits the number of words used to describe steps and also ensures that each word only has one meaning. In simplified English, 'tap' has the meaning only of 'to hit something', as in 'tap with a hammer'.

AECMA (1989). A guide for the preparation of aircraft maintenance documentation in the international aerospace maintenance language. Paris: Association Européenne des Consructeurs de Matériel Aerospatial - Contributor

Non-verbal Communication

Non-verbal communication is important in maintenance, particularly in situations where speech cannot be used, such as in noisy environments, or where people are wearing hearing protection. Non-verbal cues include gestures, facial expressions, tone of voice, and body language. If you see a colleague walking in the direction of an aircraft carrying a toolbox, it probably sends you a message about their intentions, but of course it is possible to misinterpret such messages. Particularly under time pressure or stress, we may see or hear what we expect, rather than what is actually there. The following maintenance incident illustrates the problem of misinterpreted body language.

The aircraft flight manual and pilot's operations manual, which were removed from the aircraft earlier, were on a table inside the hangar. The pilot placed his hand on the two manuals on the table noting that they were, or had been, looked at. After a few minutes I went back into the hangar where I saw the cabin door being closed and latched by one of the crew from the inside. I recall looking over at the table and seeing the manuals were not there any more, suggesting the crew had taken them with them. Just after that I noticed them on a chair.

PHYSICAL CUES

Maintenance also relies on physical cues to communicate information between maintenance personnel and to pilots. Some objects such as placards, tags or streamers attached to lockout pins have been designed specifically to communicate information.

Information is also communicated by informal cues. An open cowl, or the position of a work stand, might send a message that maintenance is underway, but sometimes the message does not get through, or we do not realize that people have come to rely on these informal cues for communication. In the following example, a chain of communication issues nearly led to an unserviceable aircraft being operated. The example involves two communication channels–first the failure to use appropriate documentation, and second an unintended message sent by the apparent physical state of the aircraft.

Aircraft arrived on Friday midday, and no time was stated when it had to be serviceable by. A job was started on an engine magneto with oral instructions, but not written in the maintenance release. At 5:00 pm, no one had asked if work on the aircraft needed to be completed, so the cowls were fitted and the aircraft placed outside without the maintenance being finished. On Sunday, I was at the airport and the pilot was doing the daily check before departure. I was able to finish the timing and refit the cowls and sign for the job. The aircraft would have been operated unserviceable.

WITHIN AND BETWEEN TEAMS

Individuals develop and coordinate activities to achieve goals by communicating with each other– by exchanging information. Effective communication is a complex process.

Some have simplistically summarized the process in these four steps:
1. Someone transmits information;
2. Someone else receives that information;
3. That the receiver understands the information;
4. Confirms to the transmitter that they have received, and understood, the information.

However, there are numerous places where this communication can break down. 'Someone transmits information' and 'someone else receives that information' sounds quite straightforward, but the person communicating the information may not be using the most appropriate means for their audience. Sending information in an email may be effective for one group, for example, but not for others, for whom a face to face toolbox talk would be more appropriate.

The choice of delivery method also depends on what has to be communicated. If it's simply technical information, or task instruction, an email or written briefing may be appropriate. However, more sensitive team building or motivational communication will require a more personal, face to face delivery, where both parties can use visual and verbal cues, such as body language, to understand how what is being said is being received.

Adapting the tone and language of your communication to your audience is also vital. The language of an academic journal. For example, is very different to that of a daily news bulletin. Academic journals are more formal, and arc often written in more technical language for a narrow, specialist audience. The daily news bulletin needs to be written in accessible, plain English, to reach as broad an audience as possible. For maintenance teams to work effectively, anyone passing on information to the team needs to ensure that the individual team members understand the meaning and context of what is being conveyed.

Regular, effective communication is vital to forming and maintaining a shared mental model, and ensuring everyone is on the same page. Good communication is also necessary for maintaining a high level of situational awareness–and having high levels of situational awareness will help teams to be more effective. Communication between teams usually occurs at shift handover.

The information conveyed usually includes:
• Tasks that have been completed;
• Tasks in progress;
• Tasks to be carried out.

Communication between teams will involve passing on written reports of tasks from one shift supervisor and, where appropriate, individuals. This means that, wherever necessary, outgoing personnel personally brief their incoming replacements. The written reports (maintenance cards, procedures, work orders, logs, etc.) and placards provide a record of work completed and yet to be completed and they provide traceability. Communication during shift handover provides continuity.

Shift Handover

At the point of shift change, the need for effective communication between the outgoing and incoming personnel in maintenance is extremely important. The absence of such effective communication has been evident in many accident reports from various industries, not just aircraft maintenance. While history is littered with past experiences of poor shift handover contributing to accidents and incidents there is little regulatory or guidance material regarding what constitutes a good handover process relevant to aircraft maintenance. This section attempts to provide guidelines on such a process and is drawn from work performed by the UK Health and Safety Executive (HSE), US Department of Energy (DOE) and the Federal Aviation Administration (FAA).

Concepts
Effective shift handover depends on three basic elements:
• The outgoing person's ability to understand and communicate the important elements of the job or task being passed over to the incoming person.

- The incoming person's ability to understand and assimilate the information being provided by the outgoing person.
- A formalized process for exchanging information between outgoing and incoming people and a place for such exchanges to take place.

The Department of Energy (DOE) shift handover standards stress two characteristics that must be present for effective shift handover to take place: ownership and formality. Individuals must assume personal ownership and responsibility for the tasks they perform. They must want to ensure that their tasks are completed correctly, even when those tasks extend across shifts and are completed by somebody else. The opposite of this mental attitude is "It didn't happen on my shift", which essentially absolves the outgoing person from all responsibility for what happens on the next shift.

Formality relates to the level of recognition given to the shift handover procedures. Formalism exists when the shift handover process is defined in the Maintenance Organization Exposition (MOE) and managers and supervisors are committed to ensuring that cross shift information is effectively delivered. Demonstrable commitment is important as workers quickly perceive a lack of management commitment when they fail to provide ample shift overlap time, adequate job aids and dedicated facilities for the handovers to take place.

In such cases the procedures are just seen as the company covering themselves as they don't consider the matter important enough to spend effort and money.

Aids to Effective Communication at Shift Handover
There are certain processes, practices and skills aids that have been found to be effective communication at shift handover.

People have to physically transmit information in written, spoken or gestured (nonverbal or body language) form If only one medium is used there is a risk of erroneous transmission. The introduction of redundancy, by using more than one way of communicating i.e. written, verbal or Non-verbal, greatly reduces this risk. For this reason information should be repeated via more than one medium. For example verbal and one other method such as written or diagrams etc. The availability of feedback, to allow testing of comprehension etc., during communication increases the accuracy. The ability for two way communication to take place is therefore important at shift handover.

A part of the shift handover process is to facilitate the formulation of a shared mental model of the maintenance system, aircraft configuration, tasks in work etc. Misunderstandings are most likely to occur when people do not have this same 'mental picture' of the state of things. This is particularly true when deviations from normal working has occurred such as having the aircraft in the flight mode at a point in a maintenance check when this is not normally done. Other considerations are when people have returned following a lengthy absence (the state of things could have changed considerably during this time) and when handovers are carried out between experienced and inexperienced personnel (experienced people may make assumptions about their knowledge that may not be true of inexperienced people). In all these cases handovers can be expected to take longer and time should be allowed for.

Written communication is helped by the design of the documents, such as the handover log, which consider the information needs of those people who are expected to use it. By involving the people who conduct shift handovers and asking them what key information should be included and in what format it should be helps accurate communication and their 'buy in' contributes to its use and acceptance of the process

Barriers to Effective Communication at Shift Handover
Certain practices, attitudes and human limitations act as barriers to effective communication at shift handover.

Key information can be lost if the message also contains irrelevant, unwanted information. We also only have a limited capability to absorb and process what is being communicated to us. In these circumstances it requires time and effort to interpret what is being said and extract the important information. It is important that only key information is presented, and irrelevant information excluded. The language we use in everyday life is inherently ambiguous. Effort, therefore, needs to be expended to reduce ambiguity by:
- Carefully specifying the information to be communicated e.g. by specifying the actual component, tooling or document,

AIRCRAFT TECHNICAL BOOK COMPANY

STATUS OF THE FACILITY	WORK STATUS	MANNING LEVELS & STATUS	PROBLEMS	INFORMATION
– Work Stands/Docking – Visitors – Construction – Health & Safety Issues	– Aircraft Being Worked – Scheduled aircraft Incoming/Departing – Deadlines – Aircraft Status vs Planned Status	– Authorization Coverage – Certifying Staff – Non-Certifying Staff – Personnel Working Overtime – Contract Staff – Sickness – Injuries – Training – Out of Base – Other Personnel Issues	– Outstanding/In-Work/Status – Solved	– AD's, SB's, etc. – Company Technical Notices – Company Policy Notices

Table 7-1. Topics to be covered during a handover meeting.

- Facilitating two way communication which permits clarification of any ambiguity. For example:
  Do you mean the inboard or out board wing flap?

Misunderstandings are a natural and inevitable feature of human communication and effort has to be expended to identify, minimize and repair misunderstandings as they occur. Communication, therefore, has to be two way, with both participants taking responsibility for achieving full and accurate communication.

People and organizations often refer to communication as unproblematic, implying that successful communication is easy and requires little effort. This leads to over confidence and complacency becoming common place. Organizations need to expend effort to address complacency by:

- Emphasizing the potential for miscommunication and its possible consequences;
- Developing the communication skills of people who are involved in shift handovers.

Shift Handover Meetings

The primary objective of the shift handover is to ensure accurate, reliable communication of task relevant information across the shifts. However, this does not recognize the user's needs for other information which may also be required to enable a complete mental model to be formed which will allow safe and efficient continuation of the maintenance process. Examples of such information could be manning levels, authorization coverage, staff sickness, people working extended hours (overtime), personnel issues etc. (*Table 7-1*)

An important aspect related to individual shift handover is when it actually begins. The common perception is that shift handover occurs only at the transition between the shifts. However, DOE shift handover standards make the point that shift handover should really begin as soon as the shift starts. Throughout their shift people should be thinking about, and recording, what information should be included in their handover to the next person or shift.

The following table lists the sort of topics that should be covered in the managers'/supervisors' handover meeting: The shift handover process should comprise at least two meetings. It starts with a meeting between the incoming and outgoing shift managers/supervisors. This meeting should be conducted in an environment free from time pressure and distractions.

Shift managers/supervisors need to discuss and update themselves on tactical and managerial matters affecting the continued and timely operation of the maintenance process. The purpose of this meeting is to acquaint themselves with the general state of the facility and the overall status of the work for which they are responsible. Outgoing managers/supervisors should summarize any significant problems they have encountered during their shift, especially any problems for which solutions have not been developed or are still in progress.

Walkthroughs

After the meeting between shift managers, and assignment of tasks, there is a need for supervisors and certifying staff to meet and exchange detailed information related to individual jobs and tasks. The most effective way to communicate this information is for the affected incoming and outgoing personnel to go over the task issues while examining the actual jobs on the hangar floor or at the workplace.

A mutual inspection and discussion of this nature is called a "Walkthrough". The following lists the sort of topics that should be covered in the supervisors/certifying staff's walkthrough meeting:
- Jobs/Tasks In Progress
- Work Cards Being Used
- Last Step(s) Completed
- Problems Encountered
- Outstanding/In-Work/Status
- Solved
- Unusual Occurrences
- Unusual Defects
- Resources Required/Available
- Location of removed parts, tooling etc.
- Parts and tools ordered and when expected
- Parts shortages
- Proposed next steps
- Communication with Planners, Tech Services, Workshops
- Communication with managers, etc.

Task Handover

The handing over of tasks from one person to another does not always occur at the point of changing shifts. Tasks are frequently required to be handed over during a shift. This section deals with two common situations. When a task is being handed over to someone who is present at the time, and when a job is being stopped partway through.

Handing Over a Task Directly to Another Person

When the task is being directly handed over to someone who is present it is done face to face using verbal and written communication. In these cases the written element is normally accomplished by ensuring that the task cards or non routine process sheets are accurately completed clearly identifying at what stage in the task the job has reached. Any deviations from normal working practices or procedures must be clearly highlighted during the walkthrough. An example of this would be if in changing a valve, a clamp not required to be removed by the maintenance manual, is disturbed to aid removal and installation. Many mishaps have occurred in these circumstances as the person taking over the job assumes that the task was being performed as per the maintenance manual, drawings, procedures etc.

Handing Over a Task for Somebody to Complete

It is not uncommon that a job is left incomplete during a shift, say in the case of someone being called away to attend to a more urgent task on another aircraft. It is often not known who will pick up the job of completing and certifying the release to service. These situations present a far greater risk and challenge to effectively communicate the stage of task accomplishment and what is required to complete the job. Face to face communication is not possible therefore total reliance has to be placed on written communication, a single medium with no redundancy and opportunity to question and test a true understanding by the person expected to finish the job.

An Accident Related to a Shift Handover

In 1991, an Embraer-120 experienced a structural breakup in flight and crashed near Eagle Lake, Texas, resulting in 14 fatalities. The night before the accident, the aircraft had been scheduled to have the deice boots replaced on the left and right horizontal stabilizers. The work was started by the evening shift, and was going to be completed by the midnight shift.

Two supervisors were on evening shift that night; one was supervising the work on the accident aircraft, while the other was overseeing a C-check on another aircraft. The aircraft scheduled for the deice boot change was brought into the hangar at around 21:30 by the evening shift. Two mechanics and a quality control inspector then used a hydraulic lift platform to get access to the aircraft's T tail, which is about 20 feet above the ground. (Under the U.S. system, inspectors oversee the work of mechanics [LAMEs] but they are not usually expected to assist mechanics with tasks.) The mechanics started removing the screws that attached the leading edge/deice boot assembly to the underside of the left horizontal stabilizer, but were slowed down by some stripped screws. Meanwhile, the inspector removed the attaching screws from the top of the left horizontal stabilizer, and then moved across to the right side and removed those screws as well, anticipating that both deice boots would be changed that night, as planned.

The hangar supervisor for the midnight shift arrived early for work and saw the evening shift mechanics working on the right deice boot. The supervisor checked the evening shift inspector's turnover form and found no write up on the aircraft—the inspector who had removed the upper screws had not yet made his log entries. The midnight shift supervisor then asked one of the evening shift supervisors (who had been working on the C-check) whether work had started on the left deice boot. The evening shift supervisor looked up at the tail where the mechanics were working and said 'no'. The midnight shift supervisor decided that the work on the left hand replacement boot would have to wait for another night.

At 22:30, the inspector who had removed the upper screws from the leading edges of both stabilizers filled out a turnover form with the entry, 'helped the mechanic remove the deice boots'. He then clocked out and went home. Later, the inspector stated that he had placed the screws he had removed from leading edges of the stabilizer in a bag and had placed the bag on the hydraulic lift.

As the evening shift prepared to go home, one of the mechanics (M1) who had removed the screws from the underside of the left horizontal stabilizer gave a verbal handover briefing to an arriving mechanic (M2) from the midnight shift. However, M2 was then assigned to work on another aircraft and was instructed to verbally brief another midnight shift mechanic (M3) on the deice boot replacement task. Then yet another mechanic (M4) was told to work on the deice boot replacement. He was told to speak with a supervisor from the evening shift to find out what work had been done. Unfortunately, this mechanic (M4) approached the C-check supervisor from the evening shift, who told him that he did not think that there would be sufficient time to change the left deice boot that night.

Personnel on the midnight shift then proceeded to remove the leading edge assembly from the right horizontal stabilizer, attach a new deice boot to it, and then reinstall the right leading edge assembly to the aircraft. The final stages of the work were done outside in the dark, as the aircraft had been pushed out of the hangar to make room for other work. None of the personnel involved noticed that screws had been removed from the upper surface of the left horizontal stabilizer, and they would have had no reason to suspect that the screws would have been missing.

Subsequently, the aircraft was cleared for flight. The first flight of the morning passed without incident, except that a passenger later recalled that vibrations had rattled his drink. He asked the flight attendant if he could move to another seat. The passenger did not tell anyone about the vibrations, and the other passengers did not notice them. The accident occurred on the next flight.

- What handover procedures might have helped to avoid this accident?
- Did problems with verbal communication contribute to the accident?
- Have you ever observed any of these problems in your own workplace?

Four Ways to Improve Shift Handover

NASA researcher Dr. Bonny Parke has studied what makes a successful handover. Whether the setting is a drilling rig, a maintenance hangar, or hospital. She has suggested the following recommendations to improve handovers:

1. Use the handover as a chance to catch errors, not just communicate information. Critically check the work of the previous shift.
2. Improve shift handover documentation. In some cases there is a reluctance to produce written records beyond the minimum requirements. However, temporary sources of information such as whiteboards can still be an important source of task handover information.
3. Have direct verbal briefings between incoming and outgoing technicians. Face-to-face handovers are standard operating procedure in many high risk industries such as nuclear power, offshore oil and air traffic control.
4. Communicate 'next steps,' not just 'work accomplished'. A good handover not only covers the work that has been accomplished, but also captures problems, possible solutions and future intentions.

Effective and Ineffective Handovers

There are at least four types of maintenance shift handover, as shown in ***Table 7-2***. In each case, the handover is indicated by a vertical line. The first shift is represented by the arrow on the left, and the second shift by the arrow on the right. Shift handovers are often focused on the transfer of information from one shift to the next, yet handovers also serve an important role as opportunities to catch and correct errors. A healthy level

FOUR TYPES OF SHIFT HANDOVERS	
→|→	Ideal handover. This is the ideal shift handover, where the task is proceeding normally before the handover and proceeds normally afterwards.
↗|↳→	Error recovery handover. Although not ideal, this is also and example of an effective handover. The task had gone off track during the first shift, but the handover provided an opportunity to identify the problem and correct it. An example is where an error made by the first shift is detected and corrected by the second shift.
→|↳→	Problem starts at handover. In this case, the task was performed correctly by the first shift, however, a problem began when the second shift took over. An example is a case when the first shift removed a faulty component for replacement. Instead of ordering an installing a serviceable component, the second shift then installed the faulty component.
↗|→	Problem starts before handover. In this case, an error was made on the first shift, and personnel on the second shift continued the error.

Table 7-2. Four types of shift handovers.

of skepticism can help to ensure that the incoming shift reviews the work of the outgoing shift, making as few assumptions as possible about its work.

WORK LOGGING AND RECORDING

This is one of the most critical aspects of communication within aviation maintenance, since inadequate logging or recording of work has been cited as a contributor to many incidents.

Even if AMTs think they are going to complete a job, it is always necessary to keep the record of work up to date just in case the job has to be handed over. This does not need to be just for shift change, but because of a rest break, illness the need to move to another more urgent task, etc.

SCHEDULED TASK CARDS

The paperwork normally associated with scheduled tasks are the task cards that are issued at the beginning of the maintenance input. These may have been written by the manufacturer, maintenance organization or the operator of the aircraft. In all cases associated task breakdown is written on the card, and assumes that the same person will start and finish the job. It was not designed to be used as a handover document.

That is not to say that it could not be the handover, or that it could not form part of one. It really depends on the circumstances.

Task cards break down jobs in to discrete stages, and ideally jobs should always be stopped at one of these stages so that the last sign off on the card is the exact stage of the job reached. In this case the card is the handover. However, a job is sometimes stopped at a

point which is between the stages identified on the card, the stage sequencing has not been followed, or a deviation from normal working has occurred. When this occurs additional written information must be used to clearly identify the point of exit from the task and what is required to complete the job and restore serviceability. Non routine cards or sheets should then be used to record and transmit the relevant information necessary. *Table 7-3* is an example of a Task Card.

Shown in *Table 7-3*, the job has not been accomplished fully due to lack of spare parts. An additional work card must be made to communicate that the Task Card does not reflect the true state of the aircraft. In this case *Table 7-4* illustrates appropriate wording.

The combination of both documents provides sufficient information for the person picking up the job to know what stage the work is up to and what is required to complete it.

COMMUNICATION

GO FAST AIRWAYS			
A/C type: B737 MP ref: MS/B737/668			
Aircraft Reg: G-OFST			
Flight Controls			
Additional Work Card Raised: Yes/No			
27-00-56	Flap Synchronizing System	Mechanic	Inspector
	a) Check the cable tensions are correct (mm 27-50-02)	B Bloggs	T. Stamp
	b) With the flaps selected up, disconnect the operating link from one transmitter gearbox only.	B Bloggs	T. Stamp
	c) Pressurize the hydraulic system and select flaps down	B Bloggs	T. Stamp
	Make sure that the flaps start to move and then the system cuts out.	B Bloggs	T. Stamp
	e) Depressurize the hydraulic system and connect the transmitter operating link.		
	f) Pressurize the hydraulic system and make sure that the flaps operate correctly.		

Table 7-3. Typical task card.

DEFECT	ACTION TAKEN	MECHANIC	INSPECTOR
Reference card 27-00-56. Card completed fully up to state D). Hydraulic system depressurized by the transmitter operating link is not reconnected. Operating link to be reconnected prior to performing stage F).			

Table 7-4. Additional task card example.

NON-SCHEDULED TASKS

Complex or lengthy nonscheduled tasks should always be broken down in to a number of discrete steps using stage or process sheets (the terminology will vary from one company to another). Many incidents have occurred when people have started a straight forward job but had to exit the task part way through without anybody to handover the task to. These situations by their nature are unplanned and are normally associated with time pressure or emergency situations. It is vital that time is taken by the person leaving the job to comprehensively record what activities have taken place and what is required to complete the job. This would be recorded on stage sheets and should emphasize any deviations from the normal or expected way of working. Management and supervisors have a responsibility to ensure that adequate time is given to maintenance staff to record their work if they require tasks to be suspended for any reason.

KEEPING UP-TO-DATE, CURRENCY

The aviation industry is dynamic: operators change their aircraft, new aircraft types and variants are introduced, new aircraft maintenance practices are introduced. As a consequence, the AMT needs to up to date.

To maintain currency, he or she must keep abreast of pertinent information relating to:
• New aircraft types or variants;
• New technologies and new aircraft systems;
• New tools and maintenance practices;
• Modifications to current aircraft and systems worked on;
• Revised maintenance procedures and practices.

AMTs can keep up-to-date by:
• Undertaking update courses;
• Reading briefing material, memos and bulletins;
• Studying maintenance manual amendments.

Responsibility for maintaining currency lies with both the individual and the maintenance organization. The AMT should keep up to date with all changes in the field. Organizations should provide the appropriate training and allow their staff time to undertake the training before working on a new aircraft type or variant. Written information should easily be accessible, and should be read.

The information should be made easy to understand (i.e., avoid ambiguity). The following situation illustrates this:

A maintenance procedure was "proscribed" (i.e. prohibited) in a service bulletin. The AMT reading this concluded that the procedure was "prescribed" (i.e. defined, laid down) and proceeded to perform the forbidden action.

DISSEMINATION OF INFORMATION

Clear dissemination of all information with in an organization forms part of its safety culture. Typically, the maintenance organization will be the sender and the AMT will be the recipient.

Part of this process should be checking that all information relating to the task has been gathered and understood. This includes checking to see if there is any information highlighting a change associated with the task (e.g. the way something should be done, the tools to be used, the components or parts involved). This especially holds true for AMTs working remotely from the base (e.g. on the line). They need to familiarize themselves with new information (on notice boards, in maintenance manuals, etc.) on a regular basis.

There should normally be someone in the organization with the responsibility for disseminating information. Supervisors can play an important role by ensuring that their team have seen and understood any communicated information. Poor dissemination of information was judged to have been a contributory factor to many accidents. Some tips for improving communication and avoiding errors.

- When you are the sender:
  - Provide information as required;
  - Deliver information clearly and concisely;
  - Verbalize plans–surprises belong at birthday parties, not in hangars;
  - Use appropriate Non-verbal communication;
  - Provide relevant information without being asked;
  - Ask for confirmation that message is understood ("what did you hear me say").
- When you are the receiver:
  - Be an active listener;
  - Acknowledge and repeat information as required;
  - Paraphrase what you have heard ("repeat what I heard");
  - Pay attention to Non-verbal as well as verbal communication;
  - Clarify uncertainties, ask questions as necessary;
  - Provide useful feedback.
- Both sender and receiver
  - Never assume;
  - Don't let the conversation end with unresolved ambiguities;
  - If a disagreement exists, take the most conservative action until more information is available.

CONCLUSION

Communication in maintenance involves not just words, whether written or spoken, but also Non-verbal cues (the body language and tone of voice) and physical cues (the positioning of tools and equipment).

- Some of the most serious maintenance related accidents have resulted from poor communication. Communication is surprisingly error prone.
- Pretask briefings should be a routine feature of maintenance tasks. Make sure everyone understands what the task will involve.
- Poor shift handover threatens maintenance quality. Consider what you can do at your workplace to prevent errors on tasks that extend over more than one shift.
- When you are the sender of a message, make sure the receiver has understood it.
- When you are the receiver, clarify the message and provide feedback to the sender. Be an active listener, and paraphrase what you are hearing.

COMMUNICATION

Question: 7-1

What are the most common ways to communicate?

Question: 7-2

What is the % of error rate in work settings for oral communication?

Question: 7-3

What is "Simplified English"?

Question: 7-4

What are the four steps in effective communication?

Question: 7-5

What information is typically received at shift handover?

Question: 7-6

What are four ways to improve shift handover?

Question: 7-7

How can AMTs keep up to date?

ANSWERS

Answer: 7-1
- Speaking
- Visual images
- Writing
- Body Language

Answer: 7-5
- Tasks that have been completed.
- Tasks in progress.
- Tasks yet to be carried out.

Answer: 7-2
The error rate in for oral communication is 3%.

Answer: 7-6
1. Use handover as a chance to catch errors.
2. Improve shift handover documentation.
3. Direct face-to-face verbal handovers.
4. Communicate next steps, not just work.

Answer: 7-3
Simplified English limits the number of words used to describe steps and ensures that each word has only one meaning.

Answer: 7-7
1. Keeping up to date on courses.
2. Reading briefing material, memos and bulletins.
3. Studying maintenance manual amendments.

Answer: 7-4
1. Someone transmits information.
2. Someone else receives information.
3. Receiver understands the information.
4. Receiver confirms to the transmitter that the information has been received.

HUMAN FACTORS

HUMAN ERROR

SUB-MODULE 08

	B1	B2

Sub-Module 08

HUMAN ERROR

Knowledge Requirements

9.8 - *Human Error*

	B1	B2
Error models and theories; Types of error in maintenance tasks; Implications of errors (i.e. accidents); Avoiding and managing errors.	2	2

HUMAN ERROR

9.8 - HUMAN ERROR

INTRODUCTION

Error is an unavoidable part of being human. Most errors have minor consequences; we burn toast, forget to pick up the dry cleaning, dial a wrong number, or make a wrong turn while driving. We can correct these errors as they are usually reversible. However, maintenance errors can have more serious consequences, and are not always caught and corrected easily.

Studies of error safety in critical industries can estimate the overall probability of errors, but cannot predict where and when an individual error will occur. *Table 8-1* shows estimated error probabilities for maintenance tasks. These estimates relate to 1960 genre technicians working on electronics and missile systems, but they are still relevant for maintenance today. For example, the probability that nuts and bolts will not be installed is estimated to be two per thousand, but the chance that they will not be properly tightened is double this. Additionally for error mitigation, when someone is checking the work of another, there is a 10 percent chance that they will miss the problem.

TASKS	Errors/1000 Tasks
Install Nuts and Bolts	2
Connect Electrical Cable	3
Install O-ring	3
Tighten Nuts and Bolts	4
Read Pressure Gauge	11
Install Lock-wire	32
Check for error in another persons work.	100

Table 8-1. Estimated error probabilities on maintenance tasks.

Human error can be seen as a natural threat that must be managed in the same way. An understanding of the risk factors for human error can help us reduce its frequency. We can also take appropriate precautions to limit its effects. The one difference is that unlike hazards in nature, human error is a constantly evolving threat, as it stems from human beings' infinite adaptability and capabilities. The maintenance errors that occur this year, with current procedures and equipment, may

be different than those that will occur next year. The solutions that work today may need to be revised and updated to continue to work in 12 months time.

Errors may be buried deep inside aircraft systems. Once maintenance is complete and the aircraft is returned to service, the chances of detecting the error before the next scheduled maintenance may be slight.

Errors can lie dormant for months or even years before causing a problem. A loosely secured nut may take months to vibrate free, and a fatigue crack caused by improper maintenance may grow slowly over years. The world's worst aviation accident involving a single aircraft occurred to a Boeing 747 that had undergone major repairs to its rear pressure bulkhead seven years before the eventual accident. The repair had involved replacing the lower half of the bulkhead; and it should have been spliced to the upper half using a single doubler plate extending under three lines of rivets. For reasons unknown, the joint relied on a single row of rivets. A fatigue fracture developed that eventually caused catastrophic failure of the rear bulkhead. The resulting damage made the aircraft uncontrollable. (*Figure 8-1*)

Many maintenance errors are found and corrected without being reported or documented. As a result, the full extent of maintenance error is unknown, and the lessons that could have been learned from each error are not always shared within the industry. Given the high probability of human error, it is remarkable that relatively few serious maintenance errors occur each year. Credit

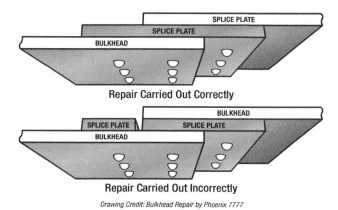

Drawing Credit: Bulkhead Repair by Phoenix 7777

Figure 8-1. The error didn't surface for 7 years. The bulkhead was secured with only a single row of rivets, rather than the double row in image shown above.

is due to the systems in place and the professionalism of maintenance personnel. Nevertheless, industries that rely on accurate and consistent human performance must be designed to deal with the inevitability of human error.

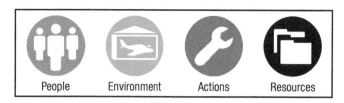

| People | Environment | Actions | Resources |

ERROR MODELS AND THEORIES

There are many published models and theories that explain why and how accidents occur. The PEAR model was addressed fully under the General section (*Sub-Module 01*). Developed by Dr. William Johnson and Dr. Michael Maddox, PEAR is not an error model as much as a way to consider human factors as a whole. However, given its importance, and the fact that it has been used for over a decade by some JAR/EASA-145 approved organizations as well as the Federal Aviation Administration (FAA), it is discussed again here.

Also in *Sub-Module 01*, The Dirty Dozen, developed by Gordon Dupont for Transport Canada, was very briefly referenced in order to list some of the factors specific to the incidents related to human factors. It will be covered in greater detail in this section. Other models that will be briefly addressed are the SHEL and HFAC models.

THE PEAR MODEL

The PEAR model of human factors in maintenance Human factors can be divided into four main topic areas using the memory prompt **PEAR**.

Application of the mnemonic 'PEAR' makes recognition of Human Factors (HF) even easier. It prompts recall of the four important considerations for HF programs: *People* who do the job; *Environment* in which they work; *Actions* they perform; *Resources* necessary to complete the job. The lists within each element are not exhaustive, but help to guide people on the human factor influences that should be considered.

PEAR was developed by Dr. Michael Maddox and Dr. Bill Johnson, specifically with maintenance in mind, as an easy way for aviation maintenance personnel to identify human factors and relate to tasks and conditions within the maintenance environment.

PEAR has been used for over a decade by some JAR/EASA 145 approved organizations and is included by the US Federal Aviation Administration (FAA) in their Maintenance Human Factors training package.

'*P*' *stands for People* (the humans in the system), with all our capabilities and limitations. It includes senses such as vision and hearing; physical characteristics such as strength and reach; as well as capabilities such as memory, communication styles, decision making, supervision and teamwork skills.

People relates to the suitability (physical, cognitive and social) of the selected personnel for a particular task. Suitability not only covers technical training but also human factors considerations such as fatigue, stress and motivations. It guides the review of the competency, supervision abilities, briefing needs, leadership skills and requirements of individuals against the task demands.

People	DOING	THINKING	INTERACTING
	–Physical Capabilities	–Knowledge	–Team Structure
	–Sensory Capabilities	–Experience	–Role Definition
	–Health	–Attitude	–Leadership
	–Training	–Motivation	–Followership
	–Current	–Confidence	–Supervision Skills vs Needs
	–Competent	–Workload	–Interpersonal Relationships
	–Authorized	–Fatigue	–Communication
	–Briefed	–Stress	–Conflicts

'*E*' *stands for the Environment* in which the work is done, not just the physical environment, but also the organization itself. The physical environment includes lighting, temperature, noise level and time of day.

The organizational environment covers issues such as supervision (quality and ratios), pressures (time, commercial and production etc.), organization and safety culture and existing organizational norms and how these will affect individual and team performance and the potential for error. The organizational environment also covers the leadership shown and the effectiveness of management in supporting positive safety behaviors.

AIRCRAFT TECHNICAL BOOK COMPANY

HUMAN ERROR

Environment	DOING	THINKING
	–Weather	–Management Style
	–Location (Inside/Outside)	–Leadership
	–Workspace	–Staffing Levels
	–Lighting	–Size/Complexity
	–Noise	–Priorities
	–Distractions	–Pressures
	–Housekeeping	–Morale
	–Hazards	–Norms
	–Shift (Day/Night/Late)	–Culture

A represents the Actions people perform. *Actions* list the requirements of a job to help to identify any specific areas that might increase the risk of error, such as ambiguous information, or complex tasks that need specialist skills and knowledge.

Actions	PHYSICAL	ORGANIZATIONAL
	–Getting Information	–Communication Requirements
	–Preparation	–Task Management
	–Briefing/Debriefing	–Supervision Requirements
	–Steps/Sequence of Activity	–Inspection Requirements
	–Application of Knowledge	–Documentation
	–Application of Skill	–Certification Requirements

The list of actions is aligned with a Job Task Analysis (JTA) process which is the standard human factors approach to identifying the knowledge, skills and attitudes necessary to perform each task in a given job. The JTA also helps identify what instructions, preparation, and task management are necessary. Some examples may include:
- Accessing/finding task specific information required
- Preparation and briefing requirements
- Identifying procedures to be followed
- Are those procedures clear and easy to follow?
- Task complexity/application of skills and knowledge
- Communication requirements (headsets required?)
- The level of supervision and inspection required (is a dual inspection needed?)
- The certification and documentation, including the complexity or user-friendly nature of the aircraft maintenance documentation.

'R' is for the Resources necessary to perform the work. *Resources* are the broadest component of *PEAR*. They can be defined as anything that the maintenance technician needs to get the job done. Resources details both the tangible items required and available, such as personnel, spares, technical manuals, tooling, and personnel protective equipment (PPE), as well as less tangible (but equally important) elements such as time and training availability.

Resources			
	–Procedures, Work Cards	–Technical Manuals	–Personnel
	–Test Equipment	–Tools	–Computers and Software
	–Paperwork and Sign-offs	–Ground Handling Equipment	–Work Stands and Lifts
	–Fixtures	–Materials	–Task Lighting
	–Training	–Quality System	–Personal Protective Equipment
	–Interpersonal Relationships	–Confidence	–Supervision Skills/Needs
	–Competence	–Workload	–Interpersonal Relationships

Time and personnel should be the first resources considered, as they are critical to the planning process of any successful job. An important resources element is focusing on identifying the areas where resources are deficient including:
- Design (work stands, tools etc.)
- Application (e.g. available, accurate procedures)
- Where additional resources (time, personnel, training, lighting, PPE and consumables) are required.

PEAR Applied to Maintenance

People
The human and the interactions between people
The part of PEAR dealing with interactions between humans is particularly important in maintenance.

Included are normal human capabilities and limitations in this part; the unaided human eye is still the main tool for inspections, yet the limitations of our vision system sometimes lead to defects being missed. We rely on short term memory each time we have to pay attention to a problem for more than a few seconds, yet the limits of our memory help explain why distractions and interruptions can be so dangerous. Good decision making is an important safety net in aviation, yet we are more likely to make poor decisions when under time pressure or stress. A 'can do' attitude is normally a positive characteristic, but in maintenance, if we attempt to operate outside our performance limitations it can lead to danger if not tempered by appropriate caution.

Environment
Physical and organizational

The maintenance environment presents numerous human factors challenges, including the need to work outside, high noise levels, temperature extremes, and at times poor lighting. All these conditions can increase the probability of error. For example, a three engine aircraft lost oil from all engines after maintenance technicians on night shift fitted magnetic chip detectors without the necessary O-rings. The work was performed outside, using the headlights of a tug for illumination. Furthermore, the technicians had no direct view of the task, and fitted each chip detector by feel, reaching inside the oil service door on each engine.

In addition to the physical environment, there is the organizational environment surrounding maintenance. Maintenance tasks are often performed under time pressure. Time pressure is a particular threat when technicians are not used to handling it, and allow it to have undue influence on their decision making. Other aspects of the organizational environment are management style, organizational culture and workplace 'norms' – the unwritten, informal work practices that members of the organization follow.

Action

Procedures, paperwork and poor design: The actions component of PEAR includes all of the hands on requirements needed to complete a task; from gathering information on tasks, identifying approved data and procedures, the physical and mental demands of the tasks, to finalizing and certifying a job complete.

The FAA has estimated that airline maintenance personnel spend between 25 and 40 percent of their time dealing with paperwork. In airlines, technicians frequently deal with maintenance documentation that is difficult to interpret, or that describes procedures in ways that appear to be out of touch with current maintenance practices. In General Aviation, the problem may be that approved documentation for older aircraft is simply not available, or is hard to obtain. Many AMTs use "black books", personal sources of unapproved technical data that may or may not be up to date. A problem faced by AMTs is a conflict between following procedures and the pressure to "get the job done".

An awareness of human factors associated with the actions required to complete a job by people at all levels of the organization can help to identify areas where the formal procedures can be approved. An accurate knowledge of task demands will help to identify informal work practices developed to meet these demands that need to be brought into alignment with formal procedures. Human factors are not just for technicians but also for managers and writers of technical documents.

Resources - A Lack of, or Deficient

Many maintenance incidents begin with a lack of necessary resources, such as time, spares, or specialized tools. Shortages will sometimes lead to work arounds or disruptions. AMTs have to deal frequently with lack of resources or equipment. Knowing how to deal with the lack of resources requires judgment that takes years to build.

THE DIRTY DOZEN

Introduction

Due to a large number of maintenance related aviation accidents and incidents that occurred in the late 1980s and early 1990s, Transport Canada identified twelve factors that degrade people's ability to perform effectively and safely, thus leading to maintenance errors. These twelve factors, known as the "dirty dozen," were eventually adopted by the aviation industry as a straight forward means to discuss human error in maintenance. It is important to know the Dirty Dozen, how to recognize their symptoms, and most importantly, know how to avoid or contain errors produced by the Dirty Dozen. Understanding the interaction between organizational, work group, and individual factors that may lead to errors and accidents. Aircraft Maintenance Technicians (AMTs) can learn to prevent or manage them pro-actively in the future.

AIRCRAFT
TECHNICAL
BOOK COMPANY

Lack of Communication (1)

Lack of communication is a key human factor that can result in suboptimal, incorrect, or faulty maintenance. (*Figure 8-2*) Communication occurs between the AMT and many different people (i.e., management, pilots, parts suppliers, aircraft services). Each exchange holds the potential for misunderstanding or omission.

But communication between AMTs may be the most important of all. Lack of communication between technicians could lead to a maintenance error and result in an aircraft accident. This is especially true during procedures where more than one technician performs the work on the aircraft. It is critical that accurate and complete information be exchanged to ensure that all work is completed without any step being omitted. Knowledge and speculation about a task must be clarified and not confused. Each step of the maintenance procedure must be performed according to approved instructions as though only a single technician did the work. The technician must see his or her role as part of a greater system focused on safe aircraft operation and must communicate well with all in that system to be effective.

- For more information on Lack of Communication, refer to *Sub-Module 07 – Communication*.

Complacency (2)

Complacency is a factor in aviation maintenance that typically develops over time. (*Figure 8-3*) As a technician gains knowledge and experience, a sense of self satisfaction and false confidence may occur. A repetitive task, especially an inspection item, may be overlooked or skipped because the technician has performed the task a number of times without ever finding a fault. The false assumption that inspection of the item is not important may be made.

Approved written maintenance procedures should be followed during all maintenance inspections and repairs. Executing the proper paperwork draws attention to a work item and reinforces its significance.

To combat complacency, a technician must train oneself to expect to find the fault that created the inspection item in the first place. He or she must stay mentally engaged in the task being performed. All inspection items must be treated with equal importance, and it must never be assumed that an item is acceptable when it has not been inspected. A technician should never sign for any work that has not been performed.

Prior to the pen touching the paper for a signature, the technician should read the item before signing and confirm it has been performed.

- For more on complacency, refer to Sub-Module 06 – Tasks.

Lack of Knowledge (3)

A lack of knowledge when performing aircraft maintenance can result in a faulty repair that can have catastrophic results. (*Figure 8-4*) Differences in technology from aircraft to aircraft and updates to technology and procedures on a single aircraft also make it challenging to have the knowledge required to perform airworthy maintenance.

All maintenance must be performed to standards specified in approved instructions. Technicians must be sure to use the latest applicable data and follow each step of the procedure as outlined. When in doubt, a technician with experience on the aircraft should be consulted. If one is not available, or the consulted technician is not familiar with the procedure, a manufacturer's technical representative should be contacted. It is better to delay a maintenance procedure than to do it incorrectly and cause an accident.

- For more on Lack of Knowledge, refer to Chapter 7 – Communication, specifically: Task Cards, Keeping Up-To-Date, Currency and Dissemination of Information.

Distraction (4)

A distraction while performing maintenance on an aircraft may disrupt the procedure. (*Figure 8-5*) When work resumes, it is possible that the technician skips over a detail that needs attention. It is estimated that 15 percent of maintenance related errors are caused by distractions.

Distractions can be mental or physical in nature. They can occur when the work is located on the aircraft or in the hangar. They can also occur in the psyche of the technician independent of the work environment. Something as simple as a cell phone call or a new aircraft being pushed into the hangar can disrupt the technician's concentration on a job.

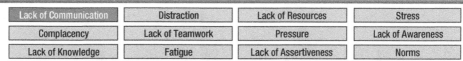

THE DIRTY DOZEN
Twelve human factors for aircraft maintenance proficiency

Lack of Communication	Distraction	Lack of Resources	Stress
Complacency	Lack of Teamwork	Pressure	Lack of Awareness
Lack of Knowledge	Fatigue	Lack of Assertiveness	Norms

Maintainers must communicate with one another and explain what work
has and has not been completed when changing shifts.

MITIGATING THE RISK

Properly use logbooks and worksheets to communicate work accomplishments.	Ensure that maintenance personnel are discussing exaclty what has been and needs to be completed to the next shift.	Never assume that the work has been completed.

Figure 8-2. Lack of communication.

THE DIRTY DOZEN
Twelve human factors for aircraft maintenance proficiency

Lack of Communication	Distraction	Lack of Resources	Stress
Complacency	Lack of Teamwork	Pressure	Lack of Awareness
Lack of Knowledge	Fatigue	Lack of Assertiveness	Norms

People tend to become overconfident after becoming proficient in a
certain task, which can mask the awareness of dangers.

MITIGATING THE RISK

Always expect to find something wrong.	Never sign off on something that you did not fully check.	Always double check your work.

Figure 8-3. Complacency.

THE DIRTY DOZEN
Twelve human factors for aircraft maintenance proficiency

Lack of Communication	Distraction	Lack of Resources	Stress
Complacency	Lack of Teamwork	Pressure	Lack of Awareness
Lack of Knowledge	Fatigue	Lack of Assertiveness	Norms

In a world of ever changing technology, maintainers must remain
up to date on current equipment and how to fix it.

MITIGATING THE RISK

| Only fix parts that you are trained to fix. | Ensure that the maintenance manual you are using is up to date. | If you do not know how to fix something, ask for help from someone who does. |

Figure 8-4. Lack of knowledge.

THE DIRTY DOZEN
Twelve human factors for aircraft maintenance proficiency

Lack of Communication	Distraction	Lack of Resources	Stress
Complacency	Lack of Teamwork	Pressure	Lack of Awareness
Lack of Knowledge	Fatigue	Lack of Assertiveness	Norms

A distraction could be anything that takes your mind off the task that is being done. Any distraction
while working can cause us to think we are further ahead in the process than we actually are.

MITIGATING THE RISK

| Once returning to the job, go back through all of the steps to ensure where you left off. | Use a detailed checklist. | Never leave tools or parts lying around. Secure them before leaving the area. |

Figure 8-5. Distraction.

Regardless of their nature, numerous distractions may occur during the course of maintaining an aircraft. The technician must recognize when attention to the job at hand is being diverted and assure that work continues correctly. A good practice is to go back three steps in the work procedure when one is distracted and resume the job from that point. Use of a detailed step-by-step written procedure and signing off each step only after it is completed.

– For more on Distraction, refer to Sub-Module 02 – Human Performance and Limitations, specifically: Information Processing.

Lack of Teamwork (5)
A lack of teamwork may also contribute to errors in aircraft maintenance. (***Figure 8-6***) Closely related to lack of communication, teamwork is required in aviation maintenance. Teamwork involves everyone understanding and agreeing on actions to be taken.

The technician primarily deals with the physical aspect of the aircraft and its airworthiness. Others in the organization perform their roles and the entire company functions as a team. Teams can win or lose depending on how well everyone in the organization works together toward a common objective.

– For more information on Lack of Teamwork, refer to Sub-Module 03 – Teamwork.

Fatigue (6)
Fatigue is a major human factor that has contributed to many maintenance errors resulting in accidents. (***Figure 8-7***) Fatigue can be mental or physical in nature. Emotional fatigue also exists and effects mental and physical performance. A person is said to be fatigued when a reduction or impairment in any of the following occurs: cognitive ability, decision making, reaction time, coordination, speed, strength, and balance. Fatigue reduces alertness and often reduces a person's ability to focus and hold attention on the task being performed.

A person's mental and physical state cycles through various levels of performance each day. Variables such as body temperature, blood pressure, heart rate, blood chemistry, alertness, and attention, rise and fall in a pattern daily. This is known as one's circadian rhythm. A person's ability to work and rest, rises and falls during this cycle. Performance counter to circadian rhythm can

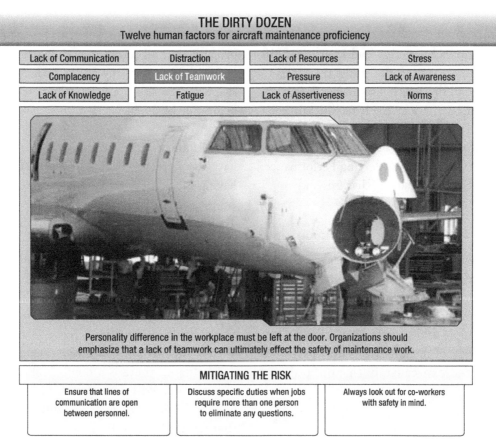

THE DIRTY DOZEN
Twelve human factors for aircraft maintenance proficiency

Lack of Communication	Distraction	Lack of Resources	Stress
Complacency	Lack of Teamwork	Pressure	Lack of Awareness
Lack of Knowledge	Fatigue	Lack of Assertiveness	Norms

Personality difference in the workplace must be left at the door. Organizations should emphasize that a lack of teamwork can ultimately effect the safety of maintenance work.

MITIGATING THE RISK

| Ensure that lines of communication are open between personnel. | Discuss specific duties when jobs require more than one person to eliminate any questions. | Always look out for co-workers with safety in mind. |

Figure 8-6. Lack of teamwork.

THE DIRTY DOZEN
Twelve human factors for aircraft maintenance proficiency

Lack of Communication	Distraction	Lack of Resources	Stress
Complacency	Lack of Teamwork	Pressure	Lack of Awareness
Lack of Knowledge	Fatigue	Lack of Assertiveness	Norms

Occupations that require an individual to work to long hours or stay up overnight can lead to fatigue. Fatigue can cause a decrease of attention and a decreased level of consciousness, which can be very dangerous when conducting maintenance.

MITIGATING THE RISK

| Be aware of the symptoms and look for them in yourself and coworkers. | Forfeit complex tasks if you know you are exhausted. | Eating healthy, exercising and regular sleep patterns can prevent fatigue. |

Figure 8-7. Fatigue.

be difficult. Shift work alone is a cause of fatigue that can degrade performance and also lead to errors. Shift work requires technicians to work during low cycles of their natural circadian rhythm. It also makes sleep more difficult when not on the job. Each technician must monitor and control his or her sleep habits to avoid fatigue.

- For more information on Fatigue, refer to Sub-Module 04 – Factors Affecting Performance, specifically: Sleep, Circadian Rhythms and Shift Work.

Lack of Resources (7)

A lack of resources can interfere with one's ability to complete a task because there is a lack of supply and support. (*Figure 8-8*) Low quality products also affect one's ability to complete a task. Aviation maintenance demands proper tools and parts to maintain a fleet of aircraft. Any lack of resources to safely carry out a maintenance task can cause both nonfatal and fatal accidents.

Parts are not the only resources needed to do a job properly, but all too frequently parts become a critical issue. AMTs can try to be proactive by checking suspected areas or tasks that may require parts at the beginning of the inspection.

Within an organization, making sure that personnel have the correct tools for the job is just as important as having the proper parts when they are needed.

Technical documentation is another critical resource that can lead to problems in aviation maintenance. When trying to find out more about the task at hand or how to troubleshoot and repair a system, often the information needed cannot be found because the manuals or diagrams are not available.

When the proper resources are available for the task at hand, there is a much higher probability that maintenance will do a better, more efficient job and higher likelihood that the job will be done correctly the first time. Organizations must learn to use all of the resources that are available and, if the correct resources

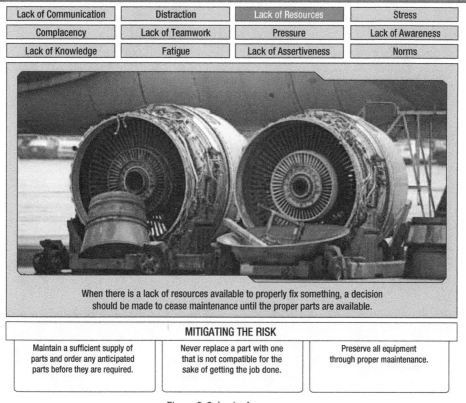

THE DIRTY DOZEN
Twelve human factors for aircraft maintenance proficiency

Lack of Communication	Distraction	Lack of Resources	Stress
Complacency	Lack of Teamwork	Pressure	Lack of Awareness
Lack of Knowledge	Fatigue	Lack of Assertiveness	Norms

When there is a lack of resources available to properly fix something, a decision should be made to cease maintenance until the proper parts are available.

MITIGATING THE RISK

| Maintain a sufficient supply of parts and order any anticipated parts before they are required. | Never replace a part with one that is not compatible for the sake of getting the job done. | Preserve all equipment through proper maaintenance. |

Figure 8-8. Lack of resources.

are not available, make the necessary arrangements to get them in a timely manner. The end result saves time, money, and enables organizations to complete the task knowing the aircraft is airworthy.

- For more information on Lack of Resources, refer to Sub-Module 06 – Planning.

Pressure (8)

Aviation maintenance tasks require individuals to perform in an environment with constant pressure to do things better and faster without making mistakes and letting things fall through the cracks. Unfortunately, these types of job pressures can affect the capabilities of maintenance workers to get the job done right. (*Figure 8-9*)

Organizations must be aware of the time pressures that are put on aircraft mechanics and help them manage all of the tasks that need to be completed so that all repairs, while done in a timely manner, are completed correctly with safety being the ultimate goal.

In an effort to combat self induced pressure, technicians should ask for help if they feel overwhelmed and under a time constraint to get a repair fixed. Another method is to have someone check the repair thoroughly to ensure that all maintenance tasks were completed correctly.

Lastly, if given a repair with a specific time limitation that you do not feel is realistic or compromises safety, bring it to the attention of the organization's management and openly discuss a different course of action.

- For more information on Pressure, refer to Sub-Module 04 – Factors Affecting Performance, specifically: Stress and Time Pressure, Time Pressure and Self Imposed Time Pressure and Work Overload.

Lack of Assertiveness (9)

Assertiveness is the ability to express your feelings, opinions, beliefs, and needs in a positive, productive manner and should not be confused with being aggressive. (*Figure 8-10*) It is important for AMTs to be assertive when it pertains to aviation repair rather than choosing or not being allowed to voice their concerns and opinions. The direct result of not being assertive

HUMAN ERROR

THE DIRTY DOZEN
Twelve human factors for aircraft maintenance proficiency

Lack of Communication	Distraction	Lack of Resources	Stress
Complacency	Lack of Teamwork	**Pressure**	Lack of Awareness
Lack of Knowledge	Fatigue	Lack of Assertiveness	Norms

Pressure to get things repaired is always present in aviation. Maintainers must not let the pressure of time constraints get in the way with safely finishing a repair.

MITIGATING THE RISK

Ensure that pressure is not self induced.	Communicate if you think you will need more time to complete a repair rather than rush through it.	Ask for extra help if time is an issue.

Figure 8-9. Pressure.

THE DIRTY DOZEN
Twelve human factors for aircraft maintenance proficiency

Lack of Communication	Distraction	Lack of Resources	Stress
Complacency	Lack of Teamwork	Pressure	Lack of Awareness
Lack of Knowledge	Fatigue	**Lack of Assertiveness**	Norms

Lack of assertiveness in failing to alert others when something does not seem right, can result in many fatal accidents. Do not let something that you know is wrong continue by ignoring that it is there.

MITIGATING THE RISK

Provide clear feedback when a risk or danger is perceived.	Never compromise your standards.	Allow co-workers to give their opinions and always accept corrective criticisms.

Figure 8-10. Lack of assertiveness.

could ultimately cost people their lives. The following are examples of how a lack of assertiveness can be offset:

- Address managers and supervisors directly by stating the problem.
  Example: "John, I have a concern with how this repair is being rushed."
- Explain what the consequences will be.
  Example: "If we continue, the result will be that the part will break sooner rather than later."
- Propose possible solutions to the problem.
  Example: "We could try doing things another way or you may want to try this way."
- Always solicit feedback and include other opinions.
  Example: "John, what do you think?"

When being assertive with coworkers or management, deal with one issue at a time rather than trying to tackle a number of problems at once. It is also important to have documentation and facts to back up your argument, which can give people a visual account of what you are trying to explain. A lack of assertiveness in failing to speak up when things do not seem right has resulted in many fatal accidents. This can easily be changed by promoting good communication between coworkers and having an open relationship with supervisors and management. Maintenance managers must be familiar with the behavior style of the people they supervise and learn to utilize their talents, experience, and wisdom. As the employees become aware of behavior styles and understand their own behavior, they see how they unwittingly contribute to some of their own problems and how they can make adjustments.

– For more information on Lack of Assertiveness. Refer to Sub-Module 07 – Social Psychology.

Stress (10)

Aviation maintenance is a stressful task due to many factors. (*Figure 8-11*) Aircraft must be functional and flying in order for airlines to make money, which means that maintenance must be done within a short time frame to avoid flight delays and cancellations. Fast paced technology that is always changing can add stress to technicians. This demands that AMTs stay trained on the latest equipment.

Other stressors include working in dark, tight spaces, lack of resources to get the repair done correctly, and long hours. The ultimate stress of aviation maintenance

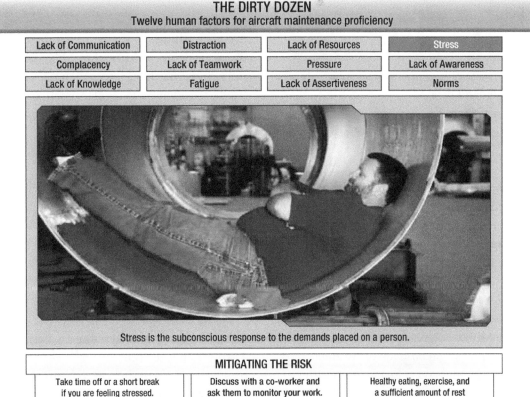

THE DIRTY DOZEN
Twelve human factors for aircraft maintenance proficiency

Lack of Communication	Distraction	Lack of Resources	Stress
Complacency	Lack of Teamwork	Pressure	Lack of Awareness
Lack of Knowledge	Fatigue	Lack of Assertiveness	Norms

Stress is the subconscious response to the demands placed on a person.

MITIGATING THE RISK

| Take time off or a short break if you are feeling stressed. | Discuss with a co-worker and ask them to monitor your work. | Healthy eating, exercise, and a sufficient amount of rest can reduce stress levels. |

Figure 8-11. Stress.

HUMAN ERROR

is knowing that the work they do, if not done correctly, could result in tragedy. The causes of stress are referred to as stressors. They are categorized as physical, psychological, and physiological stressors.

Physical Stressors
Physical stressors add to the personnel's workload and make it uncomfortable for him or her in their work environment.
- Temperature–high temperatures in the hangar increases perspiration and heart rate causing the body to overheat. Low temperatures can cause the body to feel cold, weak, and drowsy.

Psychological Stressors
- Psychological stressors relate to emotional factors, such as a death or illness in the family, business worries, poor interpersonal relationships with family, coworkers, supervisors, and financial worries.
- Work related stressors–over anxiousness can hinder performance and speed while conducting maintenance if there is any apprehension about how to do a repair or concerns about getting it done on time, and interpersonal problems. Problems with superiors and colleagues due to miscommunication or perceived competition and backstabbing can cause a hostile work environment.

Physiological Stressors
Physiological stressors include fatigue, poor physical condition, hunger, and disease.
- For more information on Stress, refer to Sub-Module 04 – Factors Affecting Performance.

Lack of Awareness (11)
Lack of awareness is defined as a failure to recognize all the consequences of an action or lack of foresight. *(Figure 8-12)* In aviation maintenance, it is not unusual to perform the same maintenance tasks repeatedly. After completing the same task multiple times, it is easy for technicians to become less vigilant and develop a lack of awareness for what they are doing and what is around them. Each time a task is completed it must be treated as if it were the first time.
- For more information on Lack of Awareness, refer to Sub-Module 06 – Tasks, specifically Repetitive Tasks.

Norms (12)
Norms is short for "normal," or the way things are normally done. *(Figure 8-13)* They are unwritten rules that are followed or tolerated by most organizations. Negative norms can detract from the established safety standard and cause an accident to occur. Norms are usually developed to solve problems that have ambiguous solutions. When faced with an ambiguous situation, an individual may use another's behavior as a frame of reference around which to form his or her own reactions. As this process continues, group norms develop and stabilize. Newcomers to the situation are then accepted into the group based on adherence to norms. Very rarely do newcomers initiate change in a group with established norms. Some norms are unsafe in that they are nonproductive or detract from the productivity of the group.

Norms have been identified as one of the dirty dozen in aviation maintenance and a great deal of anecdotal evidence points to the use of unsafe norms on the line. The effect of unsafe norms may range from the relatively benign, such as determining accepted meeting times, to the inherently unsafe, such as signing off on incomplete maintenance tasks. Any behavior commonly accepted by the group, whether as a standard operating procedure or not, can be a norm. Supervisors need to ensure that everyone adheres to the same standards and not tolerate unsafe norms. AMTs should pride themselves on following procedure, rather than unsafe norms that may have been adopted as regular practice.
- For more information on Norms, refer to Sub-Module 03 – Social Psychology, Peer Pressure and Culture and Safety Cultured.

ADDITIONAL MODELS/THEORIES
Other well respected accident models/theories that are widely referred to include the HFACS-ME Model, and the SHEL Model. They classify why human error happens in slightly different ways. A brief synopsis of each model follows:

HFACS-ME Model
Human Factors Analysis and Classification System Maintenance Extension (HFACS-ME), developed by the U.S. Naval Safety Center, is designed to identify human error that contributed to aviation maintenance occurrences and to use the information in the development of strategies to prevent such errors.

THE DIRTY DOZEN
Twelve human factors for aircraft maintenance proficiency

Lack of Communication	Distraction	Lack of Resources	Stress
Complacency	Lack of Teamwork	Pressure	Lack of Awareness
Lack of Knowledge	Fatigue	Lack of Assertiveness	Norms

After completing the same tasks multiple times, maintainers can develop a lack of awareness for what is around them. Common sense and vigilance tend to not be present because they have completed the same task so many times.

MITIGATING THE RISK

| Check to see if what you are working on conflicts with an existing modification or repair. | Always ask co-workers to check your work. | Even if you are highly proficient in a task, always have someone check your work. |

Figure 8-12. Lack of awareness.

THE DIRTY DOZEN
Twelve human factors for aircraft maintenance proficiency

Lack of Communication	Distraction	Lack of Resources	Stress
Complacency	Lack of Teamwork	Pressure	Lack of Awareness
Lack of Knowledge	Fatigue	Lack of Assertiveness	Norms

Norms is short for "normal", or the way things are normally done. They are unwritten rules that are followed or tolerated by most of the organization. Negative norms can detract from the established safety standard and cause an accident to occur.

MITIGATING THE RISK

| Ensure that everyone follows the same standard. | Be aware that just because it seems normal does not make it correct. | The easiest way of accomplishing something may not be the standard. |

Figure 8-13. Norms.

HFACS-ME classifies human error into four categories: supervisory conditions; maintainer conditions; working conditions; and maintainer acts. These are used to study the relationships among latent failures and active failures.

SHEL Model

SHEL Model, developed by Elwyn Edwards and modified by Frank Hawkins, describes how the human interacts with the system; SHEL is an acronym for software, hardware, environment and liveware (humans). The SHEL model explains how the liveware interacts with the other three elements, as well as with other human colleagues.

TYPES OF ERRORS IN MAINTENANCE TASKS

Professor James Reason is considered the leading authority on the study of human error. His books include many examples and theories explaining how and why errors occur. With this understanding accident mitigation can be developed and enforced. Starting with Professor Reason's Nut and Bolt Example, (*Figure 8-14*) we can see that most errors occur during reassembly rather than disassembly.

Professor Reason's Model of Error is a widely used categorization system for human errors shown in *Figure 8-15*. Once you have identified the type of error involved in an incident, you can then develop possible solutions.

Human errors can be divided into two basic categories, unintended actions and intended actions. "unintended action" means that we find ourselves doing a task in a way we never meant to (a slip), or we leave out a step we intended to carryout (a lapse). These errors typically occur when our attention is distracted. Intended actions can be divided into "mistakes" and violations". When we say that the action was intended, in most cases we do not mean that the person intended harm.

Figure 8-14. Professor Reason's nuts and bolt example. A bolt fitted with eight nuts can be disassembled one way, but there are over 40,000 ways in which it can be reassembled incorrectly. Consider how many more error opportunities the average general aviation aircraft presents!

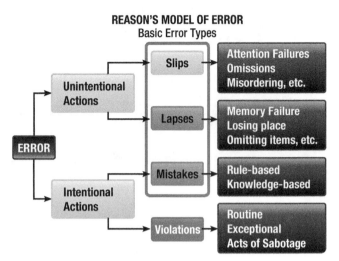

Figure 8-15. Professor Reason's model of error.

UNINTENDED ERRORS

Slips

Many people are familiar with the feeling that they have been doing a familiar task on autopilot. Slips occur when we perform a routine action that was out of place in the situation, usually because we are distracted and habit takes over. For example, in the first week of January, it is not uncommon to write the date with the previous year. Many slips in maintenance are slips of the pen, where a signature is put in the wrong place or a checklist item is missed. Slips also occur when using tools and when activating cockpit controls.

> **Example:**
> *While performing maintenance on the copilot's circuit breaker panel, the Emergency Locator Transmitter was accidentally activated via the cockpit arm/on switch. The switch was poorly located and inadequately guarded.*

Lapses

A lapse occurs when we forget to complete an action we had been intending to perform. Examples are forgetting to remove tools or rigging devices at the end of a job, forgetting to close hatches, or leaving nuts finger tight when the intention had been to torque them up. One of the most widely reported lapses in maintenance is failing to replace oil caps. Many lapses occur when the AMT has been interrupted part way through a task, often when called away to a more urgent job. They may then fail to return to the task, leave out a step, or lose their place in the task.

Example:

> *While servicing the number 2 engine, I was called away to address a problem with opening the fuel panel door. When this problem was solved, I went back to the engine and took away my oil cart and tools. Later we received feedback that the engine had experienced a loss of a gallon of oil after landing. I had no recollection of reinstalling the oil tank cap or closing the cowling door.*

INTENDED ERRORS

Mistakes

Mistakes are a type of error where the problem has occurred during thinking rather than doing. The person carries out their actions as planned, except that what they planned to do was not right for the situation. Professor Reason describes two types of these mistakes, rule based and knowledge based.

Rule Based Mistakes

Rule based mistakes occur in familiar situations where an AMT has a preexisting "rule" or guideline they use to guide their actions. This need not necessarily be a formal rule; it could be a procedure or work habit that they usually follow in that situation. The mistake happens when the rule no longer fits the situation, or the AMT misidentifies the situation.

For example, an AMT who pushed in a pulled cockpit circuit breaker without first stopping to check the cockpit control settings failed to apply a good rule or work habit to a familiar situation. In another case, an electrician wrongly assumed that a coworker had disconnected the power supply, because this was a standard work practice rule.

Example:

> *I did not check the position of the flap lever before I pushed in a cockpit circuit breaker that provided electrical power to a hydraulic pump. When the pump started, the flaps began to retract automatically. This could have caused damage to the aircraft, or injured workers.*

Knowledge Based Mistakes

Knowledge based mistakes reflect a lack of necessary knowledge, or a lack of awareness of where to find the necessary information. This is most likely to occur when a person is performing an unfamiliar task or is dealing with a non routine situation. Typically, a person who has made a knowledge based error will say they did not know about a procedure, or were confused by the task.

Example:

> *An apprentice was spraying solvent to clean an engine with the AC power on. The solvent then ignited over the engine and into an oil soaked drip tray. The apprentice had never been told of the dangers of cleaning with solvents.*

Violations

Violations are intentional deviations from procedures or good practice. In most cases, the violation occurs because the AMT is trying to get the job done, not because they want to break rules. One AMT expressed it this way: "Management tells us to follow the procedures to the letter, but then they tell us not to be obstructive and to use common sense".

Professor Reason's error model shows three types of violations "routine", "exceptional" and sabotage". Sabotage will not be dealt with here, as it is an extremely rare event in aircraft maintenance.

Routine Violations

Routine violations are the everyday deviations from procedures made to keep things moving and get the job done efficiently. While not justifying these actions, they are the easiest to understand. Routine violations are frequently so widespread in a company that they become the "normal way" that everyone works.

Researchers in Europe found that 34 percent of AMTs acknowledged that they had not strictly followed procedures in their most recent maintenance task. Common reasons for these violations are unworkable procedures and lack of resources, such as specialized tools or spares. In some cases, there is an easier way to perform the task, so that the AMT gravitates to that method. Examples are not using a torque wrench but instead judging torque by feel; or referring to a personal source of maintenance data instead of going to the maintenance manual.

Exceptional Violations

Exceptional violations are often well intentioned attempts to get the job done despite problems such as

missing documents or a shortage of parts. The AMT knows that they are deviating from procedures, but may be able to justify their actions, and usually considers that the risk is minimal. At times, for example, AMTs may be tempted to skip a required engine run to allow an aircraft to depart on time. In many cases, exceptional violations in isolation are not dangerous, yet they do reduce the margin of safety. If another problem occurs, there may be nothing standing in the way of an accident

PROFESSOR REASON'S "SWISS CHEESE" MODEL

Also known as "The Window of Opportunity" is a theoretical model that illustrates how accidents occur in organizations. The model focuses on both organizational hierarchy and human error. It states that the typical accident occurs because several (human) errors have occurred at various levels in the organization in a way that made the accident unavoidable. (*Figure 8-16*)

For example:
- Decision makers may have made poor decisions when purchasing the aircraft (fallible decisions);
- Line management may have pushed for faster turnarounds (line management deficiencies);
- Pilots may have felt pressured by a stressful climate (distraction);
- An unsafe culture of limited rest exists (preconditions);
- The pilot in the accident may have gotten distracted with other tasks prior to the accident (unsafe act);
- The aircraft systems fail in providing unmistakable warnings of the danger (inadequate defenses).

This example illustrates key concepts in the Accident Causation (Swiss Cheese) Model:
- Active errors (also called unsafe acts) are the central cause of the accident: the pilot got distracted. Had the pilot not been distracted, she/he would have prevented the accident.
- Latent errors are the remaining elements in the organization which contributed to the accident: senior managers purchasing decisions, line management pressures, unsafe climate and culture coupled with fatigue and confusing warnings. Had not any of these latent errors occurred, the accident would have been prevented.

- Windows of opportunity refer to the opportunity for those active and latent errors to contribute to an accident. Had the pilot not been distracted, he would have prevented the accident; this time. Yet, the latent errors remain unresolved, waiting for their opportunity (thus a "window of opportunity") to strike.
- Causation chain refers to the alignment of all necessary windows of opportunity at all levels in the organization, thus leading to the occurrence of a particular accident. The causes of most accidents can be traced back to "windows of opportunity" opened at all levels in the organization.

Professor Reason proposed what is referred to as the "Swiss Cheese Model" of system failure. Every step in a process has the potential for failure. The model represents a stack of slices of Swiss cheese. The holes represent opportunities for a process to fail, and each of the slices as "defensive layers" in the process. An error may allow a problem to pass through a hole in one layer, but in the next layer the holes are in different places, and the problem should be caught. Each layer is a defense against potential error impacting the outcome.

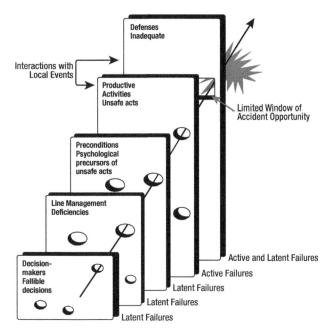

Figure 8-16. The Swiss Cheese model.

IMPLICATIONS OF ERRORS (i.e. ACCIDENTS)

As seen in Professor Reason's Swiss Cheese Model, not all errors or omissions lead to accidents.

Thankfully, most errors made by AMTs do not have catastrophic results. This does not mean that this might not be the results if the circumstances happened again in a slightly different order.

Errors that do not cause accidents, but still cause a problem are known as incidental. Some incidents are more high profile than others, such as errors causing significant in flight events that, fortunately or because of the skills of the pilot, do not become accidents. Other incidents are more mundane and do not become serious because of defenses built into the maintenance system. However, all incidents are significant to the aircraft maintenance industry, as they may warn of a potential future accident should the error occur in different circumstances. As a consequence, all maintenance incidents have to be reported. These data are used to disclose trends, and where necessary implement action to reduce the likelihood of future errors.

The greatest proportion of errors made by AMTs are spotted almost immediately and corrected. The AMT may detect his/her own error, or it may be picked up by coworkers, supervisors or quality control. In these incidents, the AMT should learn from the error and therefore (it is hoped) be less likely to make the same error again.

In an effort to identify the most frequently occurring maintenance discrepancies, the United Kingdom Civil Aviation Authority (CAA) conducted studies of aviation maintenance operations. The following list is what they found to be the most common occurring errors.

- Incorrect installation of components.
- Fitting of wrong parts.
- Electrical wiring discrepancies to include cross connections. (*Example #1*)
- Forgotten tools and parts.
- Failure to lubricate. (*Example #2*)
- Failure to secure access panels, fairings, or cowlings.
- Fuel or oil caps and fuel panels not secured.
- Failure to lock pins.

INCIDENT

On March 20, 2001 a Lufthansa Airbus A320 almost crashed shortly after takeoff because of reversed wiring in the captain's sidestick flight control. Quick action by the copilot, whose sidestick was not faulty, prevented a crash.

CAUSE

The investigation has focused on maintenance on the captain's control carried out by Lufthansa Technik just before the flight. During the previous flight, a problem with one of the two elevator/aileron computers had occurred. An electrical pin in the connector was found to be damaged and was replaced. It has been confirmed that two pairs of pins inside the connector has accidentally been crossed during the repair. This changed the polarity in the sidestick and the respective control channels "bypassing" the control unit, which might have sensed the error and would have triggered a warning. Clues might have been seen on the electronic centralized aircraft monitor screen during the flight control checks, but often pilots only check for a deflection indication, not the direction. Before the aircraft left the hangar, a flight control check was performed by the mechanic, but only using the first officer's sidestick.

Example #1. Electrical wiring discrepancies to include cross connections. A description of a Lufthansa Airbus A320 that almost crashed due to reversed wiring of the flight controls.

INCIDENT

Alaska Airlines Flight 261, a McDonnell Douglas MD-83 aircraft, experienced a fatal accident on January 31, 2000, in the Pacific Ocean The two pilots, three cabin crew members, and 83 passengers were killed and the aircraft was destroyed.

CAUSE

The subsequent investigation by the National Transportation Safety Board (NTSB) determined that inadequate maintenance led to excessive wear and catastrophic failure of a critical flight control system during flight. The probable cause was stated to be "a loss of airplane pitch control resulting from the inflight failure of the horizontal stabilizer trim system jackscrew assembly's acme nut threads. The thread failure was caused by excessive wear resulting from Alaska Airlines insufficient lubrication of the jackscrew assembly."

Example #2. Failure to Lubricate. A description of Alaska Airlines Flight 261 that crashed due to insufficient lubrication of the jackscrew assembly.

HUMAN ERROR

AVOIDING AND MANAGING ERRORS

While the aircraft maintenance industry strives toward ensuring that errors do not occur in the first place, it will never be possible to eradicate them totally. All maintenance organizations should aim toward management of errors.

A proper error management system should strive to prevent errors from occurring and eliminate or mitigate the possible negative effects of errors that do occur. To prevent errors from occurring it is necessary to predict where they are most likely to occur (i.e. reassembly of parts as in Professor Reason's nut and bolt example) and then to put in place preventative measures in an Error Management System (EMS). Professor Reason believes EMS should include measures that would:

- Minimize the error liability of the individual or team;
- Reduce the error vulnerability of particular tasks or task elements;
- Discover, assess the eliminate error producing (and violation producing) factors within the workplace;
- Diagnose organizational factors that create error producing factors within the individual, the team, the task or the workplace;
- Enhance error detection;
- Increase the error tolerance of a workplace or system;
- Make latent conditions more visible to those who operate and manage the system;
- Improve organization's intrinsic resistance to human fallibility.

ERROR MANAGEMENT SYSTEMS (EMS)

There are many techniques available for organizations to deal with the "here and now" human performance problems. There is no one best EMS. Different mixes of techniques and practices suit different organizations.

In the past EMS's tended to focus on solutions that have not proven useful. Typical problem responses included:

- Blame and Train: Discipline the individual; tell them to "be more careful", and then, if necessary institute further training.
- Write another procedure: All industries tend to write procedures to prohibit actions that have been implicated in some event or incident. The result is that the range of permitted actions is often less than the range of actions necessary to get the job done.
- Search for the "missing piece". When these measures fail (and they usually do), managers start looking for psychological ways of finding the piece that will remove violations and errors. Somewhere out there, they think is a psychologist who can come up with the "magic bullet" solution.

In contrast a Comprehensive EMS focuses most of its efforts on:

- Identifying and correcting error prone tasks.
- Improving error producing work situations.
- Identifying and correcting latent organizational conditions.

MAINTENANCE ERROR DECISION AID (MEDA)

The following system is in use in many of the world's airline maintenance facilities. It was developed by Boeing Commercial Airplanes and is designed to investigate maintenance errors and to reduce or eliminate the errors by redesigning procedures. Maintenance Error Decision Aid (MEDA) is based on three principles: "Mechanics don't intend to make mistakes"; "errors result from a variety of workplace factors, such as unclearly written manuals, poor communication between workers or improperly labeled parts"; and "management can fix the factors that contribute to errors".

Since the introduction of MEDA by Boeing, a growing number of related maintenance organizations have also adopted MEDA; a tool for investigating the factors that lead to an error, and making suggested improvements to reduce the likelihood of future errors. Boeing developed the MEDA process to help maintenance organizations identify why these errors occur and how to prevent them in the future.

Successful implementation of MEDA requires an understanding of the following:

- The MEDA Philosophy
- The MEDA Process
- Management Resolve
- Implementing MEDA
- The benefits of MEDA

The MEDA Philosophy

Traditional efforts to investigate errors are often aimed at identifying the employee who made the error. This usually results in an employee who is defensive and subjected to a combination of disciplinary action and recurrent training. Because retraining often adds little or no value to what the employee already knows, it may be ineffective in preventing future errors. In addition, by the time the employee is identified, information about the factors that contributed to the error have been lost. Because the factors that contributed to the error remain unchanged, the error is likely to recur, setting what is called the "blame and train" cycle in motion.

To break this cycle, MEDA was developed in order to assist investigators to look for factors that contribute to the error, rather than concentrate upon the employee who made the error. The MEDA philosophy is based on these principles:

- Positive employee intent (maintenance technicians want to do the best job possible and do not make errors intentionally).
- Contribution of multiple factors (a series of factors contributes to an error).
- Manageability of errors (most of the factors that contribute to an error can be managed).

Positive Employee Intent

This principle is key to a successful investigation. Traditional "blame and train" investigations assume that errors result from individual carelessness or incompetence. Starting instead from the assumption that even careful employees can make errors, MEDA interviewers can gain the active participation of the technicians closest to the error. When technicians feel that their competence is not in question and that their contributions will not be used in disciplinary actions against them or their fellow employees, they willingly team with investigators to identify the factors that contribute to error and suggest solutions. By following this principle, operators can replace a negative "blame and train" pattern with a positive "blame the process, not the person" practice.

Contribution of Multiple Factors

Technicians who perform maintenance tasks on a daily basis are often aware of factors that can contribute to error. These include information that is difficult to understand, such as work cards or maintenance manuals; inadequate lighting; poor communication between work shifts; and aircraft design. Technicians may even have their own strategies for addressing these factors. One of the objectives of a MEDA investigation is to discover these successful strategies and share them with the entire maintenance operation.

Manageability of Errors

Active involvement of the technicians closest to the error reflects the MEDA principle that most of the factors that contribute to an error can be managed. Processes can be changed, procedures improved or corrected, facilities enhanced, and best practices shared. Because error most often results from a series of contributing factors, correcting or removing just one or two of these factors can prevent the error from recurring.

The MEDA Process

To help maintenance organizations achieve the dual goals of identifying factors that contribute to existing errors and avoiding future errors, Boeing initiated the following process to avoid future errors (**Figure 8-17**)

- Event
- Decision
- Investigation
- Prevention Strategies
- Feedback

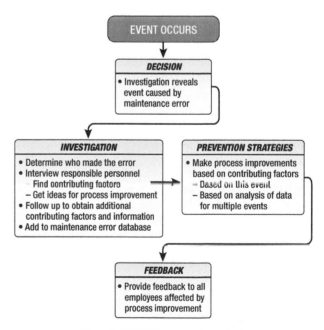

Figure 8-17. MEDA process flow chart.

Event

An event occurs, such as a gate return or air turn back. It is the responsibility of the maintenance organization to explore what problem(s) caused the events which should be investigated.

Decision

After fixing the problem and returning the airplane to service, the operator makes a decision: Was the event maintenance related? If yes, the operator performs a MEDA investigation.

Investigation

Using the MEDA results form, the operator carries out an investigation. The trained investigator uses the form to record general information about the airplane, when the maintenance and the event occurred, the event that began the investigation, the error that caused the event, the factors contributing to the error, and a list of possible prevention strategies.

Prevention Strategies

The operator reviews, prioritizes, implements, and then tracks prevention strategies (process improvements) in order to avoid or reduce the likelihood of similar errors in the future.

Feedback

The operator provides feedback to the maintenance workforce so technicians know that changes have been made to the maintenance system as a result of the MEDA process. The operator is responsible for affirming the effectiveness of employees' participation and validating their contribution to the MEDA process by sharing investigation results with them.
- Event Occurs
- Investigation finds that event was caused by mechanic inspector performance.
- Find the maintenance mechanic or inspector who did the work.
- Interview person;
  - Find Contributing Factors
  - Get Ideas for Process Improvement
- Carry out follow-up interviews, as necessary, in order to get all relevant contributing factors information
- Add the results form investigation information to a maintenance event database.
- Make process improvements;
  - Based on this event
  - Based on data from previous event
- Provide feedback to all employees affected by the process improvements.

Management Resolve

The resolve of management at the maintenance operation is key to successful MEDA implementation. Specifically, after completing a program of MEDA support from Boeing, managers must assume responsibility for the following activities before starting investigations:

MEDA is a long term commitment, rather than a quick fix. Operators new to the process are susceptible to "normal workload syndrome". This occurs once the enthusiasm generated by initial training of investigation teams has diminished and the first few investigations have been completed. In addition to the expectation that they will continue to use MEDA, newly trained investigators are expected to maintain their normal responsibilities and workloads. Management at all levels can maintain the ongoing commitment required by providing systematic tracking of MEDA findings and visibility of error and improvement trends.

Implementing MEDA

Many operators have decided to use MEDA initially for investigations of serious, high visibility events, such as in flight shut downs and air turn backs. It is easy to track the results of such investigations, and the potential "payback" is very noticeable.

In contrast, according to David Hall, deputy regional manager in the British Civil Aviation Authority (CAA) Safety Regulation Group, a high visibility event may not present the best opportunity to investigate error. The attention of operators' upper management and regulatory authorities could be intimidating to those involved in the process. In addition, the intensity of a high level investigation may generate too many possible contributing factors to allow a clear cut investigation of the event.

Hall has recommended that operators look at the broader potential for improvement by using MEDA to track the cumulative effects of less visible errors. Providing management visibility of the most frequently occurring errors can, in the long run, produce profound improvements by interrupting the series of contributing factors. According to Professor Reason, MEDA is "a good example of a measuring tool capable of identifying accident producing factors before they combine to cause a bad event."

The Benefits of MEDA

Approximately 60 operators have already implemented some or all of the MEDA processes. Participating operators have reported several benefits, including the following improvements:

- A 16 percent reduction in mechanical delays.
- Revised and improved maintenance procedures and airline work processes. A reduction in airplane damage through improved towing and headset procedures.
- Changes in the disciplinary culture of operations.
- Elimination of an engine servicing error by purchasing a filter removal tool that had not previously been available where the service was being performed.
- Improvements in line maintenance workload planning. A program to reduce on-the-job accidents and injuries based on the MEDA results form and investigation methods.

The MEDA process offered by Boeing continues to help operators of airplanes identify what causes maintenance errors and how to prevent similar errors in the future. Because MEDA is a tool for investigating the factors that contribute to an error, maintenance organizations can discover exactly what led to an error and remedy those factors. By using MEDA, operators can avoid the rework, lost revenue, and potential safety problems related to events caused by maintenance errors.

See *Appendix* pages for Maintenance Error Decision Aid (MEDA) forms.

CONCLUSION

There are varying estimates of the proportion of aircraft accidents related to maintenance errors. Maintenance errors are playing an increasing role in causing accidents. Even when accidents are averted, maintenance errors can be costly; yet no matter how hard we try, we can never completely eliminate human error.

- We need to understand how various error models work;
- Know the various types of errors and how and why they occur;

- Be aware of the typical errors that occur in maintenance and what caused the error;
- And finally, put together an EMS.

Aviation maintenance is complex, individuals perform varied tasks in an environment with time pressures, minimal feedback, and sometimes difficult conditions. Aircraft, as well as inspection and maintenance equipment, are becoming more complex. Human errors have various effects on the aviation system; from inconsequential slips, to those which affect airline efficiency and passenger convenience, to those few which ultimately result in an accident. In recognition of this, the focus is now more toward understanding the nature of human error in aviation maintenance and inspection, and improving methods for detecting and managing these errors. By understanding how various error models work, where and how human error occur, and the types of errors that occur, an effective error management system can be developed, and hopefully mitigate the likelihood of future errors.

AIRCRAFT
TECHNICAL
BOOK COMPANY

Question: 8-1

What does the PEAR Model acronym stand for?

Question: 8-2

Lack of Communication; Lack of Knowledge; Complacency are factors in which error model?

Question: 8-3

Which model explains how liveware (humans) interact with three other elements?

Question: 8-4

What are two kinds of unintended errors?

Question: 8-5

What are two kinds of intended errors?

Question: 8-6

What does the "Window of Opportunity" stand for in the Swiss Cheese Model?

Question: 8-7

MEDA is based on what three principles?

Question: 8-8

What is the MEDA Process?

AIRCRAFT
TECHNICAL
BOOK COMPANY

ANSWERS

Answer: 8-1
- People;
- Environment;
- Actions;
- Resources.

Answer: 8-2
- Lack of Communication;
- Lack of Knowledge;
- Complacency are factors in the Dirty Dozen error model.

Answer: 8-3
The SHEL Model explains how liveware interact with Software, Hardware and Environment.

Answer: 8-4
Two kinds of unintended errors are Slips and Lapses.

Answer: 8-5
Two kinds of intended errors are mistakes and violations.

Answer: 8-6
Window of Opportunity refers to mistakes that align at all levels in the organization, leading to the occurrence of an accident.

Answer: 8-7
- Positive employee intent;
- Multiple contributions cause accidents;
- Manageability of errors.

Answer: 8-8
Event;
Decision;
Investigation;
Prevention Strategies;
Feedback.

PART-66 SYLLABUS LEVELS

CERTIFICATION CATEGORY →

	B1	B2

Sub-Module 09

HAZARDS IN THE WORKPLACE

Knowledge Requirements

9.9 - Hazards in the Workplace

	B1	B2
Recognising and avoiding hazards; Dealing with emergencies.	2	2

AIRCRAFT
TECHNICAL
BOOK COMPANY

9.9 - HAZARDS IN THE WORKPLACE

INTRODUCTION

Hazards in the workplace are a health and safety issue dealing with the protection of individuals at work. Although health and safety is somewhat separate from human factors, it does very much overlap; we need to recognize where potential hazards exist and be able to establish systems or procedures that are capable of protecting workers in the same way we strive to maintain the safety of maintenance systems. This is not always possible, and when a potential hazard or accident occurs, it is necessary to have proper steps in place to deal with such emergencies.

It is not always 100% possible to remove hazards from the workplace. In such cases employees should be made aware that they exist and be given a set of procedures of how to avoid them. This can be done through training; checklists, Personal Protection Equipment (PPE) and warning signs. To be effective, warnings signs must:
- Clearly identify the hazard(s);
- Describe the danger (i.e. electric shock, radiation, etc);
- Inform employees what to do or not to do (use PPE) *Figure 9-1*.

The sign must attract the worker's attention, it must be visible and it must be understandable to the people it is aimed at. Additionally, in the maintenance industry, it must be durable enough to remain effective, often for years, in areas where dust and the elements can be present.

Positive recommendations are more effective than negative ones. For example, the statement "Stay behind yellow line on floor" is better than "Do not come near this equipment". Warning signs should contain a single word indicating the degree of risk associated with the hazard: DANGER denotes that the hazard is immediate and could cause grave, irreversible damage or injury. CAUTION indicates a hazard of lesser magnitude. The sign should also detail how to avoid or manage the risk. CAUTION signs are generally yellow and black. DANGER signs use red, black and white. (*Figure 9-2*)

Figure 9-2. "Caution" and "Danger" signs.

RECOGNIZING AND AVOIDING HAZARDS

Hazard, quite simply is the potential for harm. In practical terms, a hazard often is associated with a condition or activity that, if left uncontrolled, can result in an injury or illness. Identifying hazards and eliminating or controlling them as early as possible will help prevent injuries and illnesses.

Job Hazard Analysis (JHA) is a technique that focuses on job tasks as a way to identify hazards before they occur. It focuses on the relationship between the worker, the task, the tools, and the work environment. Ideally, after you identify uncontrolled hazards, you will take steps to eliminate or reduce them to an acceptable risk level. It can be as simple as asking yourself "Is there anything here that could hurt someone?" However, one of the best ways to determine and establish proper work procedures is to conduct a job hazard analysis. Supervisors can then use these findings to eliminate and prevent hazards in the workplace.

Figure 9-1. Signs informing employees what they should do to stay safe.

For the JHA to be effective, management must demonstrate commitment to safety and health and follow through to correct any uncontrolled hazards identified. Otherwise, management will lose credibility and employees may hesitate to go to management when dangerous conditions threaten them. When first conducting a JHA, priority should go to the following types of jobs:

- Jobs with the highest injury or illness rates;
- Jobs with the potential to cause severe or disabling injuries or illness, even if there is no history of previous accidents;
- Jobs in which one simple human error could lead to a severe accident or injury;
- Jobs that are new to your operation or have undergone changes in processes and procedures; and
- Jobs complex enough to require written instructions.

1. *Involve the team.* It is very important to involve team members in the hazard analysis process. They have a unique understanding of the job, and this knowledge is invaluable for finding hazards. Involving everyone will help minimize oversights, ensure a quality analysis, and get everyone to "buy in" to the solutions because they will share ownership in their safety and health program.

2. *Review accident history.* Review the worksite's history of accidents and occupational illnesses that needed treatment, losses that required repair or replacement, and any "near misses" – events in which an accident or loss did not occur, but could have. These events are indicators that the existing hazard controls (if any) may not be adequate and deserve more scrutiny.

3. *Conduct a preliminary job review.* Discuss hazards known to exist in current work and surroundings. Brainstorm for ideas to eliminate or control those hazards.
    - *If any hazards exist that pose an immediate danger to a team member's life or health, take immediate action to protect the worker.* Any problems that can be corrected easily should be corrected as soon as possible. Do not wait to complete the job hazard analysis. This will demonstrate commitment to safety and health and enable focus on the hazards and jobs that need more study because of their complexity. For those hazards determined to present unacceptable risks, evaluate types of hazard controls.

4. *List, rank, and set priorities for hazardous jobs.* List jobs with hazards that present unacceptable risks, based on those most likely to occur and with the most severe consequences. These jobs should be first priority for analysis.

5. *Outline the steps or tasks.* Nearly every job can be broken down into job tasks or steps. When beginning a job hazard analysis, watch the person perform the job and list each step as she/he takes it. Be sure to record enough information to describe each job action without getting overly detailed. Avoid making the breakdown of steps so detailed that it becomes unnecessarily long or so broad that it does not include basic steps. Get input from others who have performed the same job. Later, review the job steps with the team to make sure something important was not omitted. It is the job (task) that is being evaluated, not the team's job performance. The entire team should be involved in all phases of the analysis – from reviewing the job steps and procedures to discussing uncontrolled hazards and recommended solutions.

Sometimes, in conducting a job hazard analysis, it may be helpful to photograph or videotape the procedure. Visual records can be handy references when doing a more detailed analysis of the work.

IDENTIFYING WORKPLACE HAZARDS

A job hazard analysis is an exercise in detective work. The goal is to discover the following:

- What can go wrong?
- What are the consequences?
- How could it arise?
- What are other contributing factors?
- How likely is it that the hazard will occur?
- To make the job hazard analysis useful, document the answers to these questions in a consistent manner

Good hazard scenarios describe:

- Where it is happening (environment);
- Who or what it is happening to (exposure);
- What precipitates the hazard (trigger);
- The outcome that would occur should it happen (consequence), and;
- Any other contributing factors.

AIRCRAFT TECHNICAL BOOK COMPANY

Like all human factor errors in Aircraft Maintenance, rarely is a hazard a simple case of one singular cause resulting in one singular effect. More frequently, many contributing factors tend to line up in a certain way to create the hazard. Here is an example of a hazard scenario:

Example:

In the metal shop (environment), while clearing a snag (trigger), a worker's hand (exposure) comes into contact with a rotating pulley. It pulls his hand into the machine and severs his fingers (consequences) quickly.

To perform a job hazard analysis, ask:

- *What can go wrong?* The worker's hand could come into contact with a rotating object that "catches" it and pulls it into the machine.
- *What are the consequences?* The worker could receive a severe injury and lose fingers and hands.
- *How could it happen?* The accident could happen as a result of the worker trying to clear a snag during operations or as part of a maintenance activity while the pulley is operating. Obviously, this hazard scenario could not occur if the pulley is not rotating.
- *What are other contributing factors?* This hazard occurs very quickly. It does not give the worker much opportunity to recover or prevent it once his hand comes into contact with the pulley. This is an important factor, because it helps you determine the severity and likelihood of an accident when selecting appropriate hazard controls. Unfortunately, experience has shown that training is not very effective in hazard control when triggering events happen quickly because humans can react only so quickly.
- *How likely is it that the hazard will occur?* This determination requires some judgment. If there have been "near misses" or actual cases, then the likelihood of a recurrence would be considered high. If the pulley is exposed and easily accessible, that also is a consideration. In the example, the likelihood that the hazard will occur is high because there is no guard preventing contact, and the operation is performed while the machine is running. By following the steps in this example, you can organize your hazard analysis activities.

The objective should always be to eliminate the hazard. However, it is not possible to eliminate all hazards completely. Personal Protective Equipment (PPE) is the last step in protecting against workplace hazards in the JHA. Shown here is a sample form with instructions following for completing the JHA. (*Form 9-1*)

Instructions for completing a hazard analysis:

1. Identify all the different jobs that are performed at your facility.
2. Complete the Personal Protective Equipment (PPE) Hazard Analysis form for each job:
   - List the potential hazards that could occur on each type of job in the left column.
   Use one box for each hazard. Involve employees in identifying the hazards and remembering what injuries have occurred or could occur for each job.

Personal Protective Equipment (PPE)

Department	
Job	
Assessed by	
Date	

Hazard	Is there a control that could eliminate the hazard?	PPE Available	PPE Selected

Hazard Assessment

Form 9-1. JHA sample form, PPE.

– Research and determine if there are any engineering, work practice or administrative controls that could be used to eliminate or reduce each of the hazards. (OSHA says you must use these first and require PPE use as a last resort.)

– Determine if there is any PPE that would reduce the possibility of employees being injured for those hazards not corrected by the other control methods.

– List the PPE that you decide would best protect the employees from each hazard listed. Remember, the employer has the responsibility to make the ultimate decision about how employees will do the job and what protective equipment they will wear. If wearing a particular piece of protective equipment would place an employee at greater risk of injury, you would not want employees to wear that equipment. You would look for some other way to keep employees safe from the hazards.

Example:
– *You would not want employees wearing gloves to hold rough parts while operating a drill press or other fast moving/fast spinning equipment. You would want to come up with a safe way to hold the rough parts without getting cut by them and without the danger of getting a glove caught in the spinning drill bit. Two possible solutions might be to make a jig for the parts so employees don't have to hold the rough part, or send the part to be de burred before it goes to the drill press operation.*

3. After deciding on what PPE is needed at each job to keep employees safe, train employees so they know the following information:
   – When PPE is required;
   – What specific PPE is required;
   – How to use the PPE correctly;
   – How to put it on, take it off, adjust it, get a replacement and/or dispose of it;
   – Any limitations of the PPE, and;
   – The proper care, maintenance, and useful life, of the PPE.

Form 9-2 is an example of a completed JHA form with the PPE section completed.

Hazard	Is there a control that could eliminate the hazard?	PPE Available	PPE Selected
Eye damage from arc	Screens will keep others from seeing the arc	Welding hoods	Welding hood
Eye damage from welds popping as they cool		Safety glasses under hood	Safety glasses under welding hood
UltraViolet light damage to skin		Long sleeves & protective cover on face	Long sleeves & welding hood
Burns to skin & eyes from hot slag		Cotton, leather & flame resistant clothing that covers all exposed skin	Cotton pants, flame resistant long-sleeved jacket & leather boots
Foot injuries from dropping parts on them	Require parts to be handled using a lift	Steel-toed boots with metatarsal guards	Steel-toed boots with metatarsal guards
Eye damage from flying particles from grinding welds		Safety glasses & face shield	Safety glasses & face shield

Figure 9-2. Completed JHA sample form, with PPE.

DEALING WITH EMERGENCIES

Careful handling of health and safety in the maintenance environment should serve to minimize risks. However, should health and safety problems occur, all personnel should know as far as reasonably practical how to deal with emergency situations. Emergency drills are of great value in potentially dangerous environments. Everyone should take part in these whenever possible. Knowledge of what to do in an emergency can save lives.

WHAT IS AN EMERGENCY?

• An injury to oneself or to a colleague;
• A situation that is inherently dangerous, which has the potential to cause injury (such as the escape of a noxious substance, or a fire).

PREPARING FOR EMERGENCIES

Preparing for an emergency requires that you have four things in place: planning, attitude, supplies, and communications.

Planning Ahead

Having specific plans in place for various types of accidents is one of the most effective means of ensuring that accidents will be avoided when possible and handled appropriately when they do occur.

HAZARDS IN THE WORKPLACE

Attitude of Safety

In addition to planning, instilling an attitude of safety among team reduces your risk of having an emergency occur.

The Right Supplies

An important part of preparing is having the right supplies available if an emergency does happen. Minor events can become major ones if the work area does not keep emergency first aid kits and other supplies on hand at all times. (*Figure 9-3*) A member of your safety committee should be designated as a "Safety Officer" to regularly monitor and maintain first aid kits and other emergency supplies as needed. Emergency, preparation and response training for employees should include training on the proper use of emergency equipment. Some or all employees should have first aid and Cardiopulmondary Resuscitation (CPR) training. (*Figure 9-4*)

Emergency Contacts and Communications

Another essential component of preparing for emergency is having emergency contact information and communication plans in place. During training, everyone should be told who to contact and how. Employees on work sites may require wireless communications devices or other emergency communications equipment and should be trained in their safe and appropriate use. (*Figure 9-5*)

RESPONDING TO AN EMERGENCY

Depending on the situation, you may or may not need all the steps listed below, but you should follow this outline in nearly all situations:

1. *Get to a safe place.*
   Regardless of the situation, getting to a safe place after an emegency will help prevent any additional injuries from occurring. This will allow you to assess the situation and proceed.

2. *Assess the situation.*
   Is anyone injured? Has any property been damaged? Do you need to call emergency services? Answering these basic questions will determine your next steps.

3. *Call for help.*
   In any case of injury, getting professional help immediately will minimize the risks of the situation and prevent injuries from getting worse. Know the address of your workplace - and how

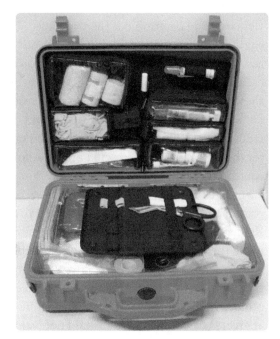

Figure 9-3. First Aid Kit should be well stocked and available. Minor emergencies can become major ones without the correct supplies on hand.

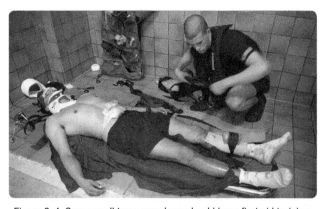

Figure 9-4. Some or all team members should have first aid training.

Figure 9-5. Employees on worksites should have emergency communication equipment.

AIRCRAFT TECHNICAL BOOK COMPANY

to give directions to get there. The emergency responders will need your name and the phone number at your location as well. When called to a large plant, fire fighters or ambulance crews can waste valuable time searching for the exact location of the emergency. It is also a good idea to direct the emergency personnel to a main entrance where someone can take them directly to the incident.

4. *Know the location of emergency equipment.*
   This can include fire extinguishers, alarms, chemical spill control materials and first aid supplies.

5. *Learn how to operate any emergency equipment.*
   Different fire extinguishers are used for different types of fires. Know how to use the safety shower and eye wash station.

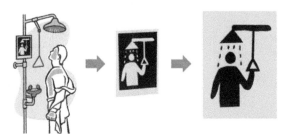

6. *Know your limits.*
   If anything beyond very simple first aid is required, always get Emergency Medical Personnel or other professionals involved right away.

7. *Know where to find the Safety Data Sheets (SDS).*
    An SDS should be available for all chemicals used in the workplace. These sheets provide valuable information which you will need in case of an accidental chemical exposure or spill.

8. *Know How To Find Emergency Exits.*
   Be aware of where the exits are and know the evacuation routes.

9. *Assist the injured.*
   Provide first aid where possible; stabilize those with major injuries.

10. *Get information.*
    Record the details of the accident while they are fresh in your mind. Time can change the way you view the situation and your memory of it, so write down all information immediately.

11. *Keep the evidence.*
    Never destroy potential evidence, the information can help to prevent further accidents. Always keep people away from potentially hazardous equipment, but do not discard or destroy it.

12. *Prevent further accidents.*
    Following an accident, you and/or your Safety Committee should quickly take action to assess the situation to prevent any further injuries. The Safety Committee may recommend long term changes, but always do what you can to keep others safe in the short term as well.

13. *Follow up.*
    File the appropriate paperwork as required and provide any assistance necessary as requested by your Safety Committee or management.

POSSIBLE WORK RELATED ACCIDENTS OR EMERGENCIES

Breathing Emergencies

Call emergency services if:
- The person stops breathing for longer than 15 to 20 seconds.
- Has severe trouble breathing, a person with this problem may:
- Have chest tightness so severe that the person is worried he or she can't keep breathing.
- Be so short of breath that she/he can't speak.
- Gasp for breath or have severe wheezing.
- Feel very anxious, afraid, or restless.

Rescue Breathing and CPR

Doing CPR the wrong way or on a person whose heart is still beating can cause serious harm. Do not do CPR unless:
- An adult is not breathing normally (may be gasping for breath).
- The person does not breathe or move in response to rescue breaths.
- No one with more training in CPR than you is present. If you are the only one there, do your best. (*Figure 9-6*)

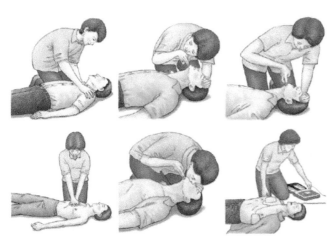

Figure 9-6. Performing CPR.

Chemical Burns

Call emergency services if:
- A strong chemical such as acid splashes into the eye.
- A large area of skin (25% of any body part) or any part of the face that is exposed to a strong acid, such as battery acid, or a caustic substance (solvents).
- A burned eye still hurts after 30 minutes after rinsing in water or wash.
- The eye is very red; has yellow, green, bloody or watery discharge; or has a gray or white discolored area.
- Vision problems occur.
- The skin is red, blistered or blackened.

Burns can occur when a harmful chemical or solvents such as a cleaning solution, gasoline or turpentine splashes into the eyes or skin, or the airways and lungs.

A burned eye may be red and watery and may be sensitive to light. If the damage is severe, the eye may look white.

Chemically burned skin may be red, blistered, or blackened, this depends on how strong the chemical was.

Call Emergency Services or Poison Control for specific advise. Have the chemical's container or label nearby.

 Right away, flush eye or skin with lots of water or eye wash kit. Use the safety shower for skin burns. Keep rinsing with water for 30 minutes or until pain stops, or help arrives.

Head Injury

Call emergency services if:
- Unconscious for more than a few seconds.
- Severe bleeding does not slow down or stop after 15 minutes of direct pressure.
- Has a seizure.
- Feels weak or numb on one side of the body.
- Double vision or trouble speaking lasts more than a minute or two.
- Seems confused, does not remember being hurt, or keeps asking the same questions.
- There is bruising around the eyes or behind one ear.
- There is a new "dent" or deformity on the skull.
- The wound needs stitches.

 A head injury may be worse than it looks. An injury that doesn't bleed on the outside may still have caused dangerous bleeding and swelling inside the skull. The more force involved, the more likely it is serious.

If the person is unconscious, assume he or she has a spinal injury. DO NOT MOVE without first protecting the neck from movement.

If there is bleeding, put firm pressure directly over the wound with a clean cloth for 15 minutes. If the blood soaks through, put another cloth over the first one.

Check for injuries on other parts of the body. The panic from seeing a head injury may cause you to miss other injuries that need attention.

Hypothermia

Call emergency services if:
- Very confused, stumbles a lot, or faints, and you suspect hypothermia.
- Hypothermia is below normal body temperature that happens when the body loses heat faster than it can produce heat. It is an emergency that can quickly lead to death.
- It does not have to be that cold to get hypothermia. You can get it at temperatures of 50°F (10°C) or even higher in wet and windy weather. It can happen in water that is 60°F to 70°F (15°C to 21°C).
- Do not ignore early warning signs. If the person starts to shiver, stumble, or respond strangely to questions, suspect hypothermia and warm quickly.

AIRCRAFT
TECHNICAL
BOOK COMPANY

Early warning signs:
- Shivering;
- Cold, pale skin;
- Lack of interest or concern;
- Clumsy movement and speech

Advanced warning signs:
- A cold belly;
- Stiff, hard muscles. Shivering may stop if temperature drops below 90°F (32.2°C);
- Slow pulse and breathing;
- Weakness or drowsiness;
- Confusion.

In the field, treatment is to stop heat loss and safely rewarm the person. Do the following:
- Get him/her out of the cold and wind;
- Remove cold, wet clothes first, and give them dry or wool clothing to wear;
- Give warm fluids and high energy foods, such as candy. Do not give food or drink if confused or has fainted. Do not give alcohol or caffeine;
- If at all possible, place in a hypotheremia wrap as shown in *Figure 9-7*.

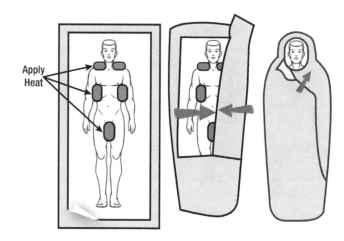

Figure 9-7. Hypothermia wrap.

Spinal Injury
Call emergency services if you think there might be a spinal injury. Symptoms include:
- Severe pain in the neck or back.
- Bruises on the head, neck, shoulders, or back.
- Weakness, tingling, or numbness in the arms or legs.
- Loss of bowel or bladder control.
- Fainting.

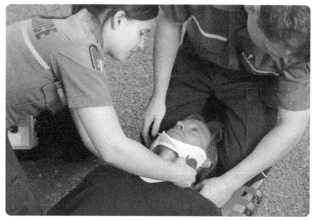

Figure 9-8. It is important to keep the spine, head, neck and shoulders in a single unit if movement is necessary to avoid paralysis.

Any accident, injury, or fall that affects the neck or back can damage the spine. It is important to keep the spine from moving and transport right way to prevent permanent loss of movement and feeling (paralysis). (*Figure 9-8*) If you suspect spinal injury:
- Do not move the unless there is an immediate threat to life, such as fire.
- If you must move the person to safety, try to move the head, neck and shoulders as a unit.

Strains, Sprains and Broken Bones
Call emergency services if:
- A bone is poking through the skin.
- The hurt limb or joint looks odd, is in a strange shape, or is out of its normal position.

- The skin over the site of an injury is broken.
- Signs of nerve or blood vessel damage, such as:
- Skin that is pale, white or blue, or feels colder than the skin on the limb that is not hurt.
- Not being able to move the limb normally because of weakness, not just pain.
- Not being able to bear weight on or straighten a hurt limb.
- Severe pain.
- Swelling within 30 minutes of the injury.
  - A *strain* is caused by over stretching or tearing a muscle or tendon. Tendons connect muscle and bone.
  - A broken bone is called a *fracture*.
  - A *sprain* is an injury to the ligaments or soft tissues around a joint. Ligaments connect one bone to another.
  - A *dislocation* occurs when one end of a bone is pulled or pushed out of its normal position.

HAZARDS IN THE WORKPLACE

All of these injuries cause pain and swelling. Unless a broken bone is obvious, it may be hard to tell whether the injury is a strain, sprain, break, or dislocation. Rapid swelling often means there is more serious injury. Most strains and sprains can be treated on site. Bad sprains, broken bones and dislocations need medical care.

Splintering

This is for short term first aid only. If a bone is broken, you can splint it so that it doesn't move until you can get the employee proper medical help.

 There are two ways to splint a limb: *Method 1:* Tie the injured limb to a stiff object, such as rolled up newspapers or magazines, a stick or cane. You can use a rope, belt, or anything else that will work as a tie. Do not tie too tightly. Place the splint so the hurt limb cannot bend. Try to splint from a joint above the suspected break to a joint below it. For example, splint a broken forearm from above the elbow to below the wrist.

Method 2: Tape a broken finger or toe to the next finger or toe, with padding between them. Tie a hurt arm across the chest to keep it from moving.

CONCLUSION

The workplace contains a wide range of hazards, some known, others less so. We have learned to control most of them, sometimes instinctively, sometimes intentionally. Given the ever increasing complexity of the aviation maintenance workplace, we can no longer rely on instinct alone. Risk must be managed just like any other business function. The negative impacts are so costly in human and financial terms.

Developing a Job Hazard Analysis with or without the help of outside experts is the best tool for avoiding risk. That being said, it is not always possible to avoid risk 100%. When something does happen, preparation and knowledge, proper equipment and drill practice can minimize the damage caused.

Additional Resources

First Aid
http://www.webmd.com/first-aid/
http://www.mayoclinic.org/first-aid/
http://www.emedicinehealth.com/first-aid-and-emergencies/center.htm

Developing a Job Hazard Analysis for Risky Tasks
https://www.osha.gov/Publications/osha3071.html

Other Helpful Sites
https://www.osha.gov
http://www.workinghealthyalways.com

Question: 9-1

When first conducting a Job Hazard Analysis, priority should go to the which types of jobs?

Question: 9-2

What usual color combination are Caution Signs? What color combination are Hazard Signs?

Question: 9-3

If you can not eliminate the hazard completely, what is the last step in the process to protect workers?

Question: 9-4

When performing a Job Hazard Analysis (JHA), what should be considered?

Question: 9-5

When preparing for an emergency, which issues should be addressed?

Question: 9-6

Who should be involved in developing a JHA?

ANSWERS

Answer: 9-1

– Jobs with the highest injury or illness rates;
– Jobs with potential to cause severe or disabling injuries or illness;
– Jobs where one simple error could lead to a severe accident or injury;
– Jobs that are new or have undergone changes;
– Jobs that are complex enough to receive written instructions.

Answer: 9-2

Caution Signs are Yellow and Black;
Danger Signs are Red, Black and White.

Answer: 9-3

The last step in the process if hazards are not completely eliminated, is the use of Personal Protective Equipment (PPE).

Answer: 9-4

JHA should take into account:
– What can go wrong?
– What are the consequences if it goes wrong?
– How could it arise?
– What are the contributing factors?
– How likely is it that the hazard will occur?

Answer: 9-5

Planning;
Attitude;
Safety supplies;
Communication channels.

Answer: 9-6

All members of the work team should be involved in developing a JHA.

Maintenance Error Decision Aid (MEDA) Results Form

Section I—General Information

Reference #: __ __ __ __ __
Airline: _____
Station of Maintenance System Failure:_____
Aircraft Type: _____
Engine Type: _____
Reg. #: __ __ __ __ __ __
Fleet Number: __ __ __ __ __ __
ATA #: __ __ __
Aircraft Zone: _____
Ref. # of previous related event: __ __ __ __ __

Interviewer's Name: _____
Interviewer's Telephone #: __ __ __ __ __ __ __ __ __
Date of Investigation: __ __ / __ __ / __ __
Date of Event: __ __ / __ __ / __ __
Time of Event: __ __ : __ __ am pm
Shift of Failure: _____
Type of Maintenance (Mx) (circle one):
　1.　Line -- If Line, what type? _____
　2.　Base --If Base, what type? _____
Date Changes Implemented: __ __ / __ __ / __ __

Section II—Event

Please select the event (check all that apply)

1. Operations Process Event
- ( ) a. Flight Delay _ days_ _ hrs._ _ min.
- ( ) b. Flight Cancellation
- ( ) c. Gate Return
- ( ) d. In-Flight Shut Down
- ( ) e. Air Turn-Back

- ( ) f. Diversion
- ( ) g. Smoke/fumes/odor event
- ( ) h. Other (explain below)

( ) 2. Aircraft Damage Event

- ( ) 3. **Personal Injury Event**
- ( ) 4. **Rework** (e.g., did not pass Ops check/inspection)
- ( ) 5. **Airworthiness Control**
- ( ) 6. **Found during Maintenance**
- ( ) 7. **Found during Flight**
- ( ) 8. **Other Event (explain below)**

Describe the incident/degradation/failure (e.g., could not pressurize) that caused the event.

Section III—Maintenance System Failure

Please select the maintenance system failure(s) that caused the event:

1. Installation Failure
- ( ) a. Equipment/part not installed
- ( ) b. Wrong equipment/part installed
- ( ) c. Wrong orientation
- ( ) d. Improper location
- ( ) e. Incomplete installation
- ( ) f. Extra parts installed
- ( ) g. Access not closed
- ( ) h. System/equipment not reactivated/deactivated
- ( ) i. Damaged on remove/replace
- ( ) j. Cross connection
- ( ) k. Mis-rigging (controls, doors, etc.)
- ( ) l. Consumable not used
- ( ) m. Wrong consumable used
- ( ) n. Unserviceable part installed
- ( ) o. Other (explain below)

2. Servicing Failure
- ( ) a. Not enough fluid
- ( ) b. Too much fluid
- ( ) c. Wrong fluid type
- ( ) d. Required servicing not performed
- ( ) e. Access not closed
- ( ) f. System/equipment not deactivated/reactivated
- ( ) g. Other (explain below)

3. Repair Failure (e.g., component or structural repair)
- ( ) a. Incorrect

- ( ) b. Unapproved
- ( ) c. Incomplete
- ( ) d. Other (explain below)

4. Fault Isolation/Test/Inspection failure
- ( ) a. Did not detect fault
- ( ) b. Not found by fault isolation
- ( ) c. Not found by operational/ functional test
- ( ) d. Not found by task inspection
- ( ) e. Access not closed
- ( ) f. System/equipment not deactivated/reactivated
- ( ) g. Not found by part inspection
- ( ) h. Not found by visual inspection
- ( ) i. Technical log oversight
- ( ) j. Other (explain below)

5. Foreign Object Damage/Debris
- ( ) a. Tooling/equipment left in aircraft/engine
- ( ) b. Debris on ramp
- ( ) c. Debris falling into open systems
- ( ) d. Other (explain below)

6. Airplane/Equipment Damage
- ( ) a. Tools/equipment used improperly
- ( ) b. Defective tools/equipment used
- ( ) c. Struck by/against
- ( ) d. Pulled/pushed/drove into
- ( ) e. Fire/smoke
- ( ) f. Other (explain below)

7. Personal Injury
- ( ) a. Slip/trip/fall
- ( ) b. Caught in/on/between
- ( ) c. Struck by/against
- ( ) d. Hazard contacted (e.g., electricity, hot or cold surfaces, and sharp surfaces)
- ( ) e. Hazardous substance exposure (e.g., toxic or noxious substances)
- ( ) f. Hazardous thermal environment exposure (heat, cold, or humidity)
- ( ) g. Other (explain below)

8. Maintenance Control Failure
- ( ) a. Scheduled task omitted/late/incorrect
- ( ) b. MEL interpretation/application/removal
- ( ) c. CDL interpretation/application/removal
- ( ) d. Incorrectly deferred/controlled defect
- ( ) e. Airworthiness data interpretation
- ( ) f. Technical log oversight
- ( ) g. Airworthiness Directive overrun
- ( ) h. Modification control
- ( ) i. Configuration control
- ( ) j. Records control
- ( ) k. Component robbery control
- ( ) l. Mx information system (entry or update)
- ( ) m. Time expired part on board aircraft
- ( ) n. Tooling control
- ( ) o. Mx task not correctly documented
- ( ) p. Not authorized/qualified/certified to do task
- ( ) q Other (explain below)

- ( ) 9. **Other** (explain below)

Did the Maintenance System Failure "fly" on the aircraft? ( ) Yes　　( ) No

Describe the specific maintenance failure (e.g., auto pressure controller installed in wrong location).

MEDA Results Form Revision L　　　　　　　1

IV. Chronological Summary of the Event, including how some Contributing Factors lead to additional
Contributing Factors

V. Summary of Recommendations

MEDA Results Form Revision L   2

Section VI—Contributing Factors Checklist

N/A __

A. Information (e.g., work cards, maintenance manuals, service bulletins, maintenance tips, non-routines, illustrated parts catalogs, etc.)

__ 1. Not understandable   __ 4. Too much/conflicting information   __ 7. Information not used
__ 2. Unavailable/inaccessible   __ 5. Update process is too long/complicated   __ 8. Inadequate
__ 3. Incorrect   __ 6. Incorrectly modified manufacturer's MM/SB   __ 9. Uncontrolled
                                                                  __ 10. Other (explain below)

Describe specifically how the selected <u>information</u> factor(s) contributed to the system failure.

Recommendations to correct the Contributing Factors listed above.

N/A __

B. Ground Support Equipment/Tools/Safety Equipment

__ 1. Unsafe   __ 6. Inappropriate for the task   __ 11. Not used
__ 2. Unreliable   __ 7. Cannot use in intended environment   __ 12. Incorrectly used
__ 3. Layout of controls or displays   __ 8. No instructions   __ 13. Inaccessible
__ 4. Out of calibration   __ 9. Too complicated   __ 14. Past expiration date
__ 5. Unavailable   __ 10. Incorrectly labeled   __ 15. Other (explain below)

Describe specifically how selected <u>ground support</u> <u>equipment/tools/safety equipment</u> factor(s) contributed to the system failure.

Recommendations to correct the Contributing Factors listed above.

N/A __

C. Aircraft Design/Configuration/Parts/Equipment/Consumables

__ 1. Complex   __ 5. Parts/equipment incorrectly labeled   __ 9. Consumable unavailable
__ 2. Inaccessible   __ 6. Easy to install incorrectly   __ 10. Wrong consumable used
__ 3. Aircraft configuration variability   __ 7. Not used   __ 11. Expired consumable used
__ 4. Parts/equipment unavailable   __ 8. Not user friendly   __ 12. Other (explain below)

Describe specifically how the selected <u>aircraft design/configuration/parts/equipment/consumables</u> factor(s) contributed to system failure.

Recommendations to correct the Contributing Factors listed above.

MEDA Results Form Revision L   3

N/A __
D. Job/Task
    __ 1. Repetitive/monotonous   __ 3. New task or task change   __ 5. Other (explain below)
    __ 2. Complex/confusing   __ 4. Different from other similar tasks
Describe specifically how the selected <u>job/task</u> factor(s) contributed to the system failure.

Recommendations to correct the Contributing Factors listed above.

N/A __
E. Knowledge/Skills
    __ 1. Technical skills   __ 4. Airline process knowledge   __ 7. Teamwork skills
    __ 2. Task knowledge   __ 5. Aircraft system knowledge   __ 8. Computing skills
    __ 3. Task planning   __ 6. English language proficiency   __ 9. Other (explain below)
Describe specifically how the selected <u>knowledge/skills</u> factor(s) contributed to the system failure.

Recommendations to correct the Contributing Factors listed above.

N/A __
F. Individual Factors
    __ 1. Physical health (including __ 5. Complacency   __ 10. Visual perception
        hearing and sight)   __ 6. Body size/strength   __ 11. Assertiveness
    __ 2. Fatigue   __ 7. Personal event (e.g., family problem, car accident) __ 12. Stress
    __ 3. Time pressure   __ 8. Task distractions/interruptions   __ 13. Situation awareness
    __ 4. Peer pressure   __ 9. Memory lapse (forgot)   __ 14. Workload/task saturation
                                                          __ 15. Other (explain below)
Describe specifically how the selected <u>individual factors</u> contributed to the system failure.

Recommendations to correct the Contributing Factors listed above.

MEDA Results Form Revision L   4

N/A __

G. Environment/Facilities

__ 1. High noise levels	__ 5. Rain	__ 9. Vibrations	__ 13. Inadequate ventilation
__ 2. Hot	__ 6. Snow	__ 10. Cleanliness	__ 14. Markings
__ 3. Cold	__ 7. Lighting	__ 11. Hazardous/toxic substance	__ 15. Labels/placards/signage
__ 4. Humidity	__ 8. Wind	__ 12. Power sources	__ 16. Confined space
			__ 17. Other (explain below)

Describe specifically how the selected <u>environment/facilities</u> factor(s) contributed to the system failure.

Recommendations to correct the Contributing Factors listed above.

N/A __

H. Organizational Factors

__ 1. Quality of support from technical organizations (e.g., engineering, planning, technical pubs)	__ 6. Work process/procedure
	__ 7. Work process/procedure not followed
__ 2. Company policies	__ 8. Work process/procedure not documented
__ 3. Not enough staff	__ 9. Work group normal practice (norm)
__ 4. Corporate change/restructuring	__ 10. Team building
__ 5. Union action	__ 11. Other (explain below)

Describe specifically how the selected <u>organizational</u> factor(s) contributed to the system failure.

Recommendations to correct the Contributing Factors listed above.

N/A __

I. Leadership/Supervision

__ 1. Planning/organization of tasks	__ 4. Unrealistic attitude/expectations	__ 6. Amount of supervision
__ 2. Prioritization of work	__ 5. Does not assure that approved process/procedure is followed	__ 7. Other (explain below)
__ 3. Delegation/assignment of task		

Describe specifically how the selected <u>leadership/supervision</u> factor(s) contributed to the system failure.

Recommendations to correct the Contributing Factors listed above.

MEDA Results Form Revision L   5

N/A __

J. Communication
  __ 1. Between departments   __ 4. Between maintenance crew and lead   __ 7. Other (explain below)
  __ 2. Between mechanics   __ 5. Between lead and management
  __ 3. Between shifts   __ 6. Between flight crew and maintenance

Describe specifically how the selected <u>communication</u> factor(s) contributed to the system failure.

Recommendations to correct the Contributing Factors listed above.

AMC	/	Acceptable Means of Compliance
AMT	/	Aviation Maintenance Technician
AOG	/	Aircraft on Ground
CO	/	Carbon Monoxide
CDU	/	Center Drive Unit
CAA	/	Civil Aviation Authority
CFR	/	Code of Federal Regulations
CPR	/	Cardiopulmonary Resuscitation
DOE	/	US Department of Energy
EMS	/	Error Management System
EASA	/	European Aviation Safety Agency
FAA	/	Federal Aviation Administration
FPI	/	Fluorescent Penetrant Inspection
H&S	/	Health and Safety
HPD	/	Hearing Protection Devices
HI	/	Heat Index
HF	/	Human Factors
HFACS-ME	/	Human Factors Analysis and Classification System Maintenance Extension
JHA	/	Job Hazard Analysis
LMEC	/	Latent Medical or Environmental Conditions
LAME	/	Licensed Aircraft Maintenance Engineer
MEDA	/	Maintenance Error Decision Aid
MOE	/	Maintenance Organization Exposition
MSDS	/	Materials Safety Data Sheets
MFF	/	Metal Fume Fever
NSC	/	National Safety Council
NTSB	/	National Transportation Safety Board
NASIP	/	National Aviation Safety Inspection Program
NDI	/	Non Destructive Inspection
OA	/	Occupational Asthma
OSHA	/	Occupational Safety and Health Administration
PEAR	/	People, Environment, Actions and Resources
PLM	/	Periodic limb movements
PPE	/	Personal Protective Equipment
RLS	/	Restless leg syndrome
SMS	/	Safety Management System
SHEL	/	Software, Hardware, Environment and Liveware
HSE	/	UK Health and Safety Executive
VWF	/	White Finger Syndrome
WOCL	/	Window of Circadian Low

# #

A

B

C

D

L

M

N

O

P

S